LAST STOP

Jan let his eyes encompass the empty horizon. Damn! It was easier in the green belt. There, though they would face constant danger, there was not the potential for mass madness—a potential exacerbated by the religious temper of the colony.

Within half a planet year, the melt and the herds would reach this spot. Before that time, they must erect fortifications.

And that girl, Angi. She had shown more signs of vertigo than most, but he had had an ulterior motive in seeking her out. She was young, pretty, and very female. With sixty-two male and only thirty-six female colonists, only those who adapted most quickly and realized the *permanence* of their plight would find wives.

Polyandry would come later. It was inevitable. *A lot of things were inevitable now that there was no hope of escape . . .*

JANDRAX

Syd Logsdon

A Del Rey Book

BALLANTINE BOOKS • NEW YORK

A Del Rey Book
Published by Ballantine Books

Copyright © 1979 by Syd Logsdon

Library of Congress Catalog Card Number: 78-71334

ISBN 0-345-28185-3

Printed in Canada

First Edition: April 1979

Cover art by Doug Beekman

A sphere floating in space, silver against a backdrop of stars.

The stars shift their colors, doppler down, out. The sphere hangs alone in darkness where *here* and *there* are concepts yet unborn. Six antennae project; it is not so much moved as displaced. First it is here, then it is there, but it never crosses the space between here and there.

Within the sphere, eight souls are busy taming the nether energies, the Synapse, so that they might emerge from otherwhere in the place of their choosing. One prowls restlessly in a place foreign to his nature, and one moves quietly in the darkness with certainty in his mind and death in his right hand.

The dark figure paused outside the room where the computer split seconds into their million component particles and prepared to extract them from netherwhere. He watched the stars fade out on the screen past Dennison's sandy head. Only a moment would pass until the stars returned and New Harmony lay below. Synapse drive can cross the galaxy in a heartbeat.

He released the trigger and hurled the grenade.

The explosion echoed through the sphere; Jan Andrax ran toward it. The bomber was gone when he reached the computer bay. Flames roared in the confined space as Staal staggered out, his clothing afire. Jan beat out the flames and leaped in to rescue his partner.

In the control room, Captain Georg Childe heard the explosion and shouted into the com. There was no answer. He tried again, then aborted without further hesitation and the stars returned.

Strange stars.

Synapse drive can cross the galaxy in a heartbeat. Four seconds had passed.

PART I

From the log of Jan Andrax,
Standard Year 873 and of the colony,
Year 1

These are the bare facts about the planet fate has chosen for our last landfall: diameter somewhat smaller than Earth, day 21 hours, year 312 Earth-standard days (a little over 356 planet days), axial tilt 32°, considerably more than Earth, resulting in greater seasonal variation. Orbital ellipticity considerably greater as well, reinforcing that effect.

Damn!

Chapter 1

The planet hung like a cold jewel in the viewport
—the last planet most of them would ever see from
orbit. Great icecaps stretched north and south, cours-
ing together to touch hands at the equator along the
one major north–south-tending mountain range. Of
course the world was uncharted. The stars hanging
beyond it were arrayed in a manner utterly strange.

The planet's oceans were gone—locked into the
massive polar caps—and what remained as seas
would be extremely saline. The air would be
very dry; it was likely that rain never fell, only winter snows.

A cold, barren, forbidding world hanging close in
to a cool sun.

Jason D'Angelo was on watch, his 10-mm double-
barreled rifle cradled across his arm, when the leer
broke cover. He heard its splayed webbed feet splat-
ting on the muddy ground before he saw it. Lucien
Dubois saw it at the same time and leaped back from
the carcass he was gutting, bringing his knife up in
futile defense.

Jason fired as the leer began its final rush toward
the unprotected colonist. The leer staggered and
turned on his new tormentor. Blood discolored the
bird's iridescent pink feathers, but did nothing to
slow its charge. Jason aimed more carefully this time
and shot it fair in the chest, just left of its massive
sternum. The leer went down like a felled tree and
Jason broke open his rifle.

The dead leer's mate broke cover before he had time to reload. Jason spun around in time to see the bird explode soundlessly, scattering flesh and entrails across the clearing. For a moment Jason was too stunned to react, then he realized that Jan Andrax stood beside him holding his express pistol. "You'd better finish reloading, Jase," he said and turned away. Jason punched two new shells into the breech of his rifle and was grateful that there was no one to see how his fingers trembled.

Andrax swallowed hard. It had been a close thing for D'Angelo and through no fault of his own. The 10-mm rifle was part of a small consignment for New Harmony; it was designed for simplicity and reliability, not firepower. A two-shot weapon simply was not adequate for an untamed world.

He holstered his express pistol. Dubois had returned to gutting the herby, but the violence of his motions showed the degree to which he had been frightened. That was good; the fright was inevitable but he continued to function in spite of it. Jan made no move to aid him, but continued to scan the surrounding bushes.

Jason wiped blood from his face. It had been that close. Express pistols were a specialty tool issued only to Scouts. By twisting a dial with his off hand, Jan could tailor projectile size and velocity to the target at hand. If the dial was not touched the maximum charge was sufficient to stop a terrestrial elephant three times over. Jan had not dialed.

Jason searched for an appropriate response to the situation, but could only say, lamely, "Thanks."

Jan smiled, but his eyes never left the perimeter of the clearing. "When I was scouting on Lando, I nearly got myself killed a couple of times, and—you know what? You never get used to it.

"However, you do learn not to let it throw you off. Put it out of your mind and get back to watching so that I can help get this carcass back to base."

Stung, Jason turned his attention back to duty. They slung the field-dressed herby on a pole and returned to camp, passing through the tangle field that so far had kept the native carnivora at a reasonable distance.

The landing craft was in orbit, having carried up a load of meat to feed the colonists on the *Lydia*. In the early years of star travel each ship had been a self-contained ecosystem, but with the advent of the Synapse and nearly instantaneous interstellar travel, ships turned to processed food and mechanical recirculation of air and water. Three weeks in orbit had completely exhausted the *Lydia*'s food stores.

Jan Andrax dropped onto a camp stool made from the stems of a tough, fast-growing bush and began scraping from his boots the mucilaginous substance exuded by the local ground cover. Jason relinquished his rifle and another pair of colonists left to hunt. Hunting was a full-time occupation for those who had to supply meat to the many overhead.

Jan stopped scraping long enough to assure himself that they were not going to be overheard, then asked, "Any word on the computer?" Jason shook his head. Jan swept the area about him with a searching look before returning to his boots. Jason realized that he probably was not even aware of that mannerism. Jan was a Scout, trained for just such an environment; Jason was the ship's astrogator. He had never felt more out of place or useless.

"They'll never fix the computer," Andrax continued. "You know that, don't you?" Jason nodded. Both of them had seen the computer bay after the explosion. The Synapse jump had lasted over four seconds; the longest previous jump, under carefully controlled conditions, had been of less than a second's duration and it had driven a ship clear outside the galactic lens. Instantaneous travel had its complications. "Jase, how long before Captain Childe comes to his senses and announces to the colonists that this is to be their new home—and ours?"

"It's awfully hard for him to accept."

6

"Humph. It's hard for *me* to accept. This is one hell of a final landfall, but facts are facts."

Jason held his peace, not wanting to criticize the captain. Already lines had been drawn, separating the seven living crew members from the colonists. Andrax was supernumerary, a Scout hitching a free ride from Banex to Aleph Prime via New Harmony. He did not fit either classification but Jason was thankful to have him aboard. How they could hope to survive without his professional expertise was a question he preferred not to face.

"Well," Jan continued, "if the announcement hasn't been made yet, I intend to explore those so-called ruins tomorrow. Once Childe starts ferrying down colonists, there won't be any time. Want to come along?"

Jason said that he did, but later, as sounds from the temporary jungle that surrounded them kept him awake, he wondered why.

The landing craft descended with the sunrise, carrying half a dozen new colonists. Jan met them at the ramp, giving concise orders and turning them over to their more experienced comrades. There was something vaguely familiar about the fourth colonist, but a closer look did nothing to spark Jan's memory. The man was named Adrian Dumezil, of indeterminate middle age and pleasant, but undistinguished features. Jan motioned him out of line, for no other reason than that he had caught his eye, and he had already intended to take one of the new colonists with him.

Jason and Dumezil carried packs; Jan did not. It was Jan's order, strictly enforced, that those whose job it was to guard should not be burdened otherwise. More than one colonist had felt Jan's anger after relaxing his guard momentarily to help a companion.

It takes only a moment of inattention to bring death on a new planet.

Jan set the pace, stepping out sharply. The land

rolled gently and their vision was restricted by the fast-growing bushes, but not so restricted as it would have been even a week earlier. The herds of herbys, trihorns, and humpox had battered and browsed the bushes into a thick, tangled, dying mat.

Jason quizzed Adrian, seeking out the climate of opinion overhead.

"No one knows what to believe," Dumezil replied. "The official word is that there was a computer malfunction, but rumor says that it was a major explosion and that we are stranded. Frankly, rumor is more convincing." He looked sideways at Jan to ask, "Which is it?"

"Explosion," Jan answered. Jason winced. "We are here for as long as we survive. Childe is a fool. When he gets around to telling the truth, he will have alienated all the colonists just when he needs them most . . . hit the deck!"

The Scout's sudden change of tone caught his companions flat-footed. Jan had already gone to cover beneath a siskal bush with his express pistol at the ready. Jason and Dumezil tumbled in to join him.

There was a rustling in the brush and a coughing grunt, then a group of trihorns came into sight. They were magnificent beasts, fully two meters high at the shoulders with shaggy manes sloping away to low, naked rumps. Their heads were massive and sported a single central horn projecting forward and trifurcating, one point up and two down.

They were mammals, of course. Hair, live birth, warm blood, and suckling are all characteristics evolved in just such a harsh, cold climate. It was clearly a family group: a monstrous bull, an uddered female with two hornless suckling calves at her side, and a monopointed adolescent.

The three men remained motionless until they had passed.

Adrian Dumezil wiped sweat from his face and grinned. "Now there goes a beast I wouldn't like to tackle. I thought this was a desert planet."

"It is," Jan replied. Because of the cold, and because most of the planet's water was tied up in the massive icecaps, it never rained. Much of the year the land was barren desert, but in the winter ice crystals formed in the upper atmosphere and fell as sleet, snow, and hail. Throughout the winter this accumulated and, with the coming of spring, melted to release water for the growth of plants. Within a few weeks of its coming, the melt would pass, leaving desert again.

This was the stationary view. From space the area of the melt was a broad band of green moving slowly southward. Along the route of the green belt moved massive herds of herbivores and attendant carnivores, caught up in a perpetual migration.

The landing craft had set down on the forefront of the green belt three weeks earlier and already the herds had largely passed by. Within days it would be necessary to move the hunting base southward several hundred kilometers.

They marched in silence then, broken only when Jan or Jason showed Adrian how to recognize siskal, lal, and greenhorn bushes and the tracks of the three major herbivores and their corresponding carnivores: the leers—huge, toothed, flightless birds—and long-necks, whose sinuous necks and compact musculature made them particularly dangerous, and the tiny, scavenger krats.

They were ruins. Despite the stats he had studied, Jan had not believed that they would be.

The ruins topped a butte that rose perhaps a hundred meters above the surrounding countryside and extended for about a square kilometer. It took a sharp scramble to reach them and, when they had, there was little to reward the climb. Few of the stone walls remained more than waist-high and most of the city/castle/fortification/whatever was reduced to rubble by time. There was little to show what manner of creature had inhabited the place until Jason found a mural on one of the plastered inner walls. Its faded pigment showed a potbellied, winged mammal with what appeared to be grasping hands. In a corner of the mural, isolated by fractured plaster, were the foot and ankle of another creature. Jan stared long at it, then rummaged without success for the lost pieces of plaster. Adrian joined him, asking "Why so intent?"

"Because," Jan answered, "that foot looks uncannily human." They did not find the missing plaster, nor anything else to identify the masters of the ruin.

It was well past noon when they left the site, intent on returning to the camp by nightfall. Jason seemed troubled and managed to fall back slightly to speak to Jan alone.

"Something you said to Dumezil bothers me. You said that we would be here as long as we survive. What exactly did you mean by that?"

Jan did not answer at once. His restless eyes never stopped their circuit. "Jase, do you know what the mortality rate is for Scouts on a new planet? Trained men whose whole life is dedicated to survival?"

"No."

"Ten percent for each new planet."

Jason greeted that with stunned silence.

"Jase, the first planet I explored, three of my twenty companions died; nor was it an exceptionally dangerous planet. On my second planet two of my friends were cut down before my eyes by an innocuous-looking flying mammal whose poison was deadly to humans.

"I came through my third planet with no particular difficulty, but on the last one I tangled with a large, horned herbivore during my first day planet-side and left in a coma. I spent a total of two hours on her surface.

"Those were planets which had been properly scanned from orbit. I was working with trained and experienced Scouts and the latest of equipment. Here . . ."

Jan broke off as something caught his attention. What it was, Jason could not tell, but it apparently

10

posed no danger because the Scout relaxed again and continued, hardly aware of the interruption.

"Here, I'd give odds that there won't be a human alive inside ten years."

Chapter 2

Computer printout found folded and placed in the log of Jan Andrax

Monists. Full title, *Universal Monists.* A religious group founded by Louis Dumezil in S.Y. 767. The premise of this group is that all religions were founded by the same spirit (deity?) and that a true religion can be found by collating the elements common to all religions while rigorously discarding those elements confined to particular religions or families of religions. The text containing this distillate was published S.Y. 767, hence the founding date, and was called the *Monomythos.* Dumezil further refined his text through eleven revisions culminating in the *Grand Monomythos* in S.Y. 801. After his death, further revisions led to the splitting of the Universal Monists into denominations based on increasingly fine points of doctrine. Each sect publishes its own subtly different *Monomythos.* As of S.Y. 872 four hundred distinct Universal Monist sects were known. Several ecclesiastical wars have been fought among them, the most violent being on Hallam in S.Y. 851–859.

Unbroken by vegetation, a land of gently rolling hills stretched to the horizon. To the east, ramparts of hills rose, similarly naked, and in the distance one could see the massed green and white above the melt line where trees grew through the perpetual snow. Near at hand the ground was tortured and broken with the fossil prints of last melt's herd.

Angi Dumezil negotiated the ramp gingerly, bowed under the weight of her share of the supplies. *Papa* Marcel, leader of the colonists, and her brother Anton stayed near her; the others were strangers. Jan Andrax directed their egress and hurried them beyond the flash perimeter. When they were sheltered below a nearby hillock, he signaled to the landing craft and it leaped skyward, then rolled into the gentle arc that would carry it northward to the green belt to take on meat for the colonists remaining overhead.

Angi shaded her eyes against the cool sunlight until she could no longer see the departing speck.

Andrax had called them into a circle. He squatted negligently, scratching a map into the ground. "We are here, two kilometers above the camp. The river Lydia runs here, though it is little more than a stream this time of year. We've hardly begun with shelters. There is no wood nearby; until the melt comes and we can float it down from the hills, we are experimenting with rammed earth and adobe."

Angi looked around, drawing her jacket tighter about her. Now that the landing craft had gone, there was no work of man and no bit of vegetation to break the endless monotony of the rolling land. The whole of her vision was encompassed by gray-brown soil and red-brown rocks. She closed her eyes tightly against a feeling of vertigo and missed the rest of the instructions Andrax was giving.

They shouldered their burdens and walked to the base. Whenever they topped a rise, hundreds of square kilometers lay stretched out before them, but all so uniform that the eye refused to acknowledge the scale. No haze muted the distance.

Andrax did not move to aid the colonists with

12

their burdens, but paced up one side of the column and down the other with his express pistol ready at hand. What creature could possibly inhabit that wilderness, Angi could not imagine.

By the time they reached camp, Angi was suffering from thirst. Though the day was cool, the air seemed utterly devoid of moisture and sucked away her body fluids with every breath. Rows of adobe bricks lay at the water's edge, all split and crumbled in the cold, dry air.

A single building stood, a long, low dormitory framed with driftwood from the river and coated with dried mud. There was a fire built of the dung cakes that lay so abundantly on all the hills.

After they had eaten and drunk, Andrax set them to work. It was a kindness; once her hands were busy, Angi's unease abated somewhat. She worked with a girl of her own age, Helene, unpacking and cataloging the crates they had brought. Jan drifted by from time to time, once stopping to ask, "Feeling better?"

"What do you mean?" Angi replied, turning away to mask her irritation.

"Don't be evasive. I'm not much of a psychologist, but I'm the best we have. It's part of my training. Tell me what you felt hiking in. Vertigo?"

She nodded.

"What do you know about sensory deprivation?"

"Enough to recognize my own problem," she snapped.

Andrax smiled. "Then you know that drawing into yourself at this moment is the worst thing you can do. Would it help to know that almost all the colonists feel as you do?"

Her shrug said *I don't know.*

"Talk to Helene about it. Odds are she'll share your feelings and you'll both be better for the conversation."

Jan continued to circulate, looking for trouble. At this crucial point, the psychological state of his charges bore more potential for danger than the environment. Later, when the first groups had begun to adjust, they

13

would form a stable core on which the remaining colonists could lean.

He let his eyes encompass the empty horizon. Damn! It was easier in the green belt where the danger was constant, but where there was not the potential for mass madness—a potential exacerbated by the religious temper of the colony.

Within half a local year, the melt and the herds would reach this spot. Before that time, they must erect fortifications. For that they would need timber, but as yet he could spare no timber-cutting parties.

That girl, Angi. She had shown more signs of vertigo than most, but he had had an ulterior motive in seeking her out. She was young, pretty, and very female. With sixty-two male and only thirty-six female colonists, only those who adapted most quickly and realized the *permanence* of their plight, would find wives.

Polyandry would come later. It was inevitable.

Every day the landing craft brought down new colonists. Nur Mohammet and Tennyson Risley of the crew were working on a ground-effect machine to be used for surface transportation. Relying only on the landing craft to transport their daily meat would be unwise.

A month passed. The skimmer took over the run to the green belt—a shorter run every day. Only Captain Childe remained in orbit, unwilling yet to give up on the *Lydia*.

Jan took time every day to spend at least a few minutes with Angi, not neglecting to give attention to the half-dozen other girls of appropriate age. In his estimation, none of the others matched Angi, but one never knew. Angi's suitors were increasing in number and boldness.

Jan had just managed to catch Angi alone when Tenn Risley found him.

"Jan. It's Jason. He's been killed."

Jan felt himself stiffen up inside. Of all his companions, the only one he would have called a friend was Jason. Angi touched his arm, saying, "I'm sorry."

"How did it happen?"

"Tree fell on him." Jason had piloted the skimmer with a crew of colonists up into the mountains on a cutting expedition. "Dubois just called in to tell us. Someone has to hike up there because none of the cutters can run the skimmer."

"Was anyone else hurt?" Angi asked.

"They didn't say, so I suppose not. Oh, one of your brothers was on the crew, wasn't he?"

"Yes. Jean."

Jan and Tenn started at daybreak. The skimmer required a fairly flat roadway, so it had followed the river Lydia. Jan and Tenn would have had to follow it anyway to stay near water. The air was so dry that they required vast quantities of liquid.

The cutters met them and Jan offered each a brief nod. He knew everyone by now. It was his job to do so. Jean Dumezil, Angi's younger brother, wore his usual flat expression, but Alexandre Chambard and Lucien Dubois were clearly moved.

They had covered the body with a sleeping bag. Jan threw it back and grimaced. Jason was badly crushed and his clothing was matted with blood. There was no need to look closer, but habit made Jan do so. He found tiny bits of moss embedded in the wounds near the base of Jason's skull, but nowhere else. Suspicion was mirrored in his expression, and he tried to suppress it. The colonists had levered the bole off Jason but had not moved him. The bole was bare of moss.

The old, down limbs scattered about on top of the snow were not. Happenstance? Or had Jason been clubbed into unconsciousness and left in the path of the tree?

"How the hell did this happen?"

Dumezil answered, "He was gathering down wood and apparently didn't hear the warning." Chambard and Dubois looked uneasy, but nodded their agreement.

"Who cut the tree?"

15

"I did," Dumezil said.

Angi left her family to join Jan. Even now he kept vigil, never trusting the land around him. The line of mourners circled beneath the low hillock where he watched. Angi stopped beside him and laid her hand gently on his arm. "He was the first," Jan said, "but he won't be the last."

There were two bundles and two graves. Tom Dennison's body had been coated with polyfoam and irradiated to preserve it after the explosion in the computer bay. Caught up in the press of immediate needs, the colonists had not taken time to begin a cemetery until now.

A white, amorphous, anonymous bolus of plastic lay beside one grave; a hide-wrapped bundle lay beside the other. *Both killed by the same mad act—and every other death this planet will witness attributable to the one who stranded us here.* Jan grimaced and started down the hill.

Marcel Dumezil, the leader of the Monists, read the service. Jan doubted that Dennison would have appreciated it. He was a Pentecostal Baptist from NorAm, the only one aboard the *Lydia* who had actually been born on Earth.

As for Jason, he had been a Pertoskan Monist. He had argued into the night with Alex Chambard the day before he died, disputing the points of doctrine which separated his sect from the Benedictine Monism embraced by the colonists.

Coincidence?

Dumezil closed his *Monomythos* and stepped back. Alex and Lucien lowered Jason into the earth; Nur and Valikili lowered Tom Dennison. Then Valikili took a shovel and gently broke away a portion of the polyfoam. "Once the man is gone," he said, "it is wrong to preserve the body."

Jan nodded, all the time knowing that the permafrost would preserve both bodies better than any work of man.

They shoveled in the cold, dry earth. Jan watched

16

the colonists as the graves were filled, wondering who had thrown the bomb, and why. It had to be on everyone's mind.

Tears flowed freely as Henri Staal saw his watchmate under. He had mostly recovered from his burns, though he would always bear scars. Jan touched his shoulder as they left the cemetery to say, "I'm sorry."

Staal looked around at the bleak horizon and shuddered. "Why, Jan? Why would anyone do this?"

There was no answer he could give.

Chapter 3

Valikili crouched lower. Claude Delacroix was on sentry duty and, sleepy though he might be, the colonist would take great pleasure if he were to catch Val slipping past the cordon. No punishment would be exacted, of course, but considerable embarrassment—for Helene as well as himself. Delacroix and Helene had once had an understanding. On Bordeaux, before their emigration, they had talked of marriage. Helene had told Valikili of this, but their new situation had thrown all old understandings into question.

Delacroix disappeared behind the half-completed stockade wall and Valikili trotted down toward the river. There was no cover, so stealth was pointless. He had to drop below the break in the land before the sentry returned.

He did not see the figures that followed him.

Valikili was the *Lydia*'s third engineer and, though he felt allegiance to his fellow crewmembers, he was adapting rapidly. He was a short, powerful Polynesian; his face reflected his open nature and his body was a statue sculpted in muscle. He was not unaware of his beauty.

17

Nor were the colonist girls. He had his pick, and he had chosen Helene Dumezil.

Helene was not related to Angi or the patriarch. Two-thirds of the colonists were named Dumezil after Louis Dumezil, the founder of their religion, and there weren't enough first names to keep track by.

Valikili reached the river and started upstream toward their meeting place. A fringe of tough vegetation grew along the water's edge—the only vegetation that survived into the dry season. He avoided its suggestive darkness. No incident had yet justified the sentries that Jan had placed, but Valikili, more than the colonists, respected his judgment. Besides, there were the *precursors;* everyone was speculating as to what had happened to whoever built those ruins.

It was unlikely that this generation would find time to explore that mystery and the next generation— what would they be like, so unnaturally cut off from the rest of mankind. Valikili shuddered at the thought.

His mood was anything but playful when he reached their appointed meeting place. Helene was not there. Valikili squatted to wait, uneasily watching the shadows. He regretted arranging the tryst and regretted his mood, which might well ruin it anyway. Something about the shadows of the vegetation near the water looked odd. He tried to ignore it, but his eyes kept straying back: It looked like a crumpled, human form.

Precursor? A superstitious shiver ran up his spine, followed immediately by a more urgent fear. Helene?

He approached the shadow warily. It was—something. Closer; it was a humanoid form, sprawled face downward.

"Helene?"

It was. He dropped beside her, feeling for her carotid pulse and drew back a hand sticky with blood. "No!" He felt closely, found a lump at the base of her skull, detected a weak pulse.

Something moved in the bushes.

He crouched over her and snarled, "Come out of there!" A figure rose, human, but anonymous in the darkness. It raised a knife to catch the moonlight.

Valikili crouched lower, trying to remember the rudimentary fighting skills he had been taught so many years before. The figure advanced and Valikili circled, trying to draw him out into the light.

Something struck him from behind, knocking him to his knees, while his first adversary swept the knife forward, cutting him from elbow to wrist. Valikili felt the spurt of blood and knew that he had only moments before losing consciousness.

He ducked his head, jamming his sliced arm into his stomach to stop the bleeding. A club caught his shoulder and drove him down, rolling him over. The knife drove into his back, aimed for his kidney but deflected by his movement. He rolled forward and the knife thrust in again, tearing the muscles of his back and glancing off a rib.

He plunged into the vegetation, struck the river and fell forward. The stream was small, but swift. It carried him southward, bouncing him against rocks and mudbars. Blackness swept in and receded. He caught at the bottom with scrabbling fingers and reached the bank, then rolled in the mud trying to stop the wounds in his back. He felt consciousness slipping again and rolled over on his face, forcing his open forearm into the mud and pressing it under the weight of his body.

Marcel LaBarge found him, but Valikili remembered nothing until the pain of movement awakened him. By that time a dozen men had gathered around and Dr. Marcuse was bandaging his arm with practiced efficiency. "There," he said, seeing Val's eyes open "that should hold you together long enough to get you back to camp. What did you tangle with—a longneck?"

"Forget it, Doc." It was Jan and his eyes bore fire. "Don't pretend ignorance. You know damned well those are knife slashes."

Valikili reached up with his free hand and Jan took it. "Helene?"

"She staggered into camp with a concussion. Nothing very serious, but it set off our search for you."

Valikili relaxed into unconsciousness. Marcuse

looked sideways at Jan and said, "Don't make a big thing out of this. You have to expect violence when the sex ratio is this disturbed."

"Just a jealous boyfriend. Is that what you're saying?"

"Yes."

"Stick to your stitches, Doc. You don't have the faintest damned idea what's going on."

The snow came nearly every night, layer upon thin layer, moisture squeezed from the upper atmosphere by the cold.

The palisade was nearly completed and there were some makeshift brush and mud shelters inside. Everyone was constantly cold. They had collected only enough furs for blankets, though soon they would have enough to start making clothing. The coveralls that were standard for shipboard wear were scant protection here, and Dr. Marcuse had two cases of pneumonia as well as the slowly recovering Valikili housed in his makeshift infirmary in the hold of the landing craft.

Nur Mohammet closed the hide curtain behind him and crossed to the central fire. He shook out the blanket he had wrapped about him and laid it near the hearth, then dropped onto it. Marcel Damle stirred the dung-cake fire and asked, "How is he?"

"Better. He was actually in good spirits today."

"That's a switch," Risley said.

Nur grinned. It always took Tenn by surprise when Nur's solemn face opened up. "His girl came to see him."

"Helene?" Tenn asked.

"She took her sweet time," Jan added. "Why?"

"She told Valikili that she was scared to go to him before."

"Bull breeze."

"No, Tenn," Jan said, "I believe her. She really was scared."

Henri looked up from his work; his scars showed pale in the firelight as he asked, "Was she raped?"

Jan shrugged, "Marcuse knows, but he's not talking. With only six or eight decent looking women in a colony full of young bucks, you figure it out."

Staal cursed and his hands shook. Marcel touched his knee and spoke softly, "Henri, marry Marie. Don't wait until someone else takes her away from you. Also, once you are living with her, you can protect her."

Nur turned to Jan. "You don't think rape was the motive, do you?"

Jan shook his head. "I think it was an excuse, an afterthought, and a diversion. I think they were out to kill Val."

"Because he is one of the crew?"

"No. Because he isn't a Monist."

After three months, Marcel Dumezil reinstituted the Sabbath. From a practical standpoint it was a good system. Planning and good judgment depend on frequent periods of rest; otherwise the immediate but trivial has a tendency to swamp more important long-range considerations.

With that in mind, Jan walked with Angi to the field beyond the palisade after the service. Everyone in the colony seemed to have the same idea and soon the snowy earth was dotted with furry shapes, each sitting a little apart from his neighbor, relishing privacy after the cramped squalor of life within the palisade.

"Jan," she said, placing her hand on his arm, "you look worried. Today is a day of rest, so please relax. I spend half my time worrying that either you or *Papa* will crack under the strain you are carrying."

Jan looked up at the broad, barren expanse of snow, at the mountains beyond, where the scars of their cutting lay, and behind at the palisade. They had done well; yet it was not any natural disaster that worried him. He feared the seeds of dissension carried within the group.

"Nur and Tenn did not attend the service," Jan pointed out. "How will your people feel about that?"

She shrugged. "It is their right. We are not barbarians, you know."

Jan said nothing. Angi scooped up snow, balled it angrily and tossed it down. "You think we are, don't you?"

"Huh? Are what?"

"Barbarians. You think Nur and Tenny are in danger from us because they are of a different religion. Where did you ever get such an idea? What have we done to make you think that of us. Or are you just prejudiced?"

"I never said any such thing," Jan replied, but he was thinking of Jason. And he was remembering Hallam.

There was a holiday air about the camp. Raoul La-Barge was a trained geologist; he had explored the hills back of the settlement—keeping mainly to the creeks for reasons of future transportation—and he found an outcropping of iron ore, something infinitely more precious than gold.

Jan gave himself the afternoon off for good behavior and took Angi out. They went on skis, for the snow was half a meter deep. She looked beautiful to him, though, in truth, imagination played a good part in that. She was dressed as everyone else, Jan included, in a trihorn parka cut from the hairy shoulder section of the hide, wide herbyskin trousers, and boots made from the hairless rump section of trihorn hide. Only her face and a few wisps of hair showed from beneath her krathide cap. Angi's beauty was a thing remembered from warmer days, not something available for immediate experience.

They talked of things which had become commonplace and of the future of the colony. They spoke a little of a more personal future and she remained very close to him while he cursed the cold that imprisoned them in their furry armor.

Jan was not a man given to noticing natural beauty. It was not a thing to brag about, but his profession had made him very businesslike in his relationship to the environment. Were that not so, he would long since have been dead. Yet he had come to love their cold, barren world—but never so much as on that afternoon when imprisoned passion was transmuted into softer feelings as they skiied hand in hand across the clean, white plains, moving in a common rhythm.

Chapter 4

Four local months after the *Lydia* was stranded, the snows began to melt. At first only the surface melted during the day, refreezing at night. For a time, footing was treacherous. Then there came a time when the water did not completely refreeze, merely skimmed over. Finally the palisade was surrounded by a vast ocean of snowmelt, extending to the horizon and breaking like an inland sea against the foothills. The river swelled until it filled its kilometer-wide bed with a violent rush of ice-clogged, mud-brown water.

Even while the land was still covered, the first vegetation appeared; leaves and flowers sprang up on every withered bush and fresh shoots thrust out, growing at an unbelievable rate. When the water receded to mud, the gluegrass burst the bounds of earth, soft, stubby spikes of mucilaginous growth that clung to and fouled the legs of those who ventured out.

Then came the leers and the first wave of krats. Angi Dumezil watched the huge flightless birds from the palisade as they slogged about, buoyed up by their webbed feet. The hunters were only a hundred kilometers north of the settlement now, which eased the strain on the failing skimmer. In the palisade, preparations were being made to greet the main herd when it came. The mammalian herbivores would not arrive until the mud had dried enough to support their hooves.

Off to the north a small, deep lake in the shape of a perfect square marked the permafrost cellar dug earlier by the men. Now water filled, it would be filled with meat in the coming weeks and sealed with a covering of soil.

In the courtyard below, Jan was conducting classes in archery. The bows were of fiberglass formed from native sand by the lifeboat's power pile. The arrows were tipped with the first native iron to have been smelted. Angi watched the men fire a volley, pride of community mingled with pride in her man. Jan had not asked her to marry him, but she expected the invitation any day—perhaps after the herds had passed and a measure of leisure had returned.

She returned to the task at hand, pouring boiling water through layers of ash to obtain the materials from which to make lye soap. She was a pioneer and the daughter of pioneers; hard work was nothing new to her. Still, she had never been in a situation before where such a sense of urgency infused every act. It had welded them, crew and colonists alike, into a tightly knit community with the common purpose of survival. There was little bickering and an almost unnatural peace, due in part to the heritage of Benedictine Monism shared by all but the crew.

People no longer spoke of the fact that they were marooned. Angi, innocent of the complexities of spaceflight, found it strange that the uninjured ship orbiting Harmony—as they were coming to call the planet—was useless without the flight computer. And no one talked about the fact that they had been stranded by a deliberate act. Everyone knew that one of their number was responsible for their exile, but no one had the courage to speculate as to whom.

She looked up as Adrian Dumezil and Alexandre Chambard arrived from the outside with a fresh barrel of water. They had it slung from two poles. Working together they transferred its contents to the stationary barrel above her kettle.

Chambard wandered off, but Adrian Dumezil remained to pass the time. He was chewing a siskal twig, which the colonists had discovered to be bitter and mildly narcotic. Those who had smoked tobacco before had, to a man, taken up chewing siskal. He was one of the many to have adopted the surname of Mentor Louis Dumezil and was unrelated to Angi.

Adrian watched the archers at their practice as Angi fed the fire. When she stood up and stretched, he grinned down at her and asked, "Has Andrax proposed yet?"

Angi flushed, then laughed, taking no offense. "No, not yet."

"I wonder if he will?" He did not seem to notice Angi's blush, nor recognize the inappropriateness of his comment; rather, he seemed absorbed in some problem beyond her knowledge.

"Why do you say that, Adrian?"

"That isn't my name."

Now she was completely bewildered.

"My name is Sabine Conners. I knew Andrax as a boy, though he has not recognized me yet. I wore a different face then, as well as a different name. Plastic surgery. I was a wanted man."

"Why tell me that?"

He chuckled. "Why not? I'm not wanted any more, now that we're stranded here.

"But your question was the right one. Why not isn't an answer to why. I tell you this because I've known you since you were a child and I don't want to see you hurt. Have you ever wondered why Jan keeps himself so aloof?"

"He's awfully busy, and he has a lot of responsibilities."

Sabine shook his head. "Jan doesn't trust us because we are Monists."

"I know, but I don't know why."

Sabine sucked on the twig for a moment longer before throwing it away. "Jan Andrax was born on Hallam. His father was the leader of the Danneline Monists in their guerilla war against the Pertoskans. He was orphaned there."

Angi was shocked. The Hallam war had been one of the bitterist in recent history. Then she made another connection. "You said you knew him as a boy. That was after Hallam?"

Sabine chuckled again. "Delicately put. No, I fought right beside him and his father. That is what I was wanted for."

"Then Jan was wanted, too?"

"No, and that's something I don't understand. He still carries the face and name he was born with and he is a Scout. How did he ever get into the Scouts with his record?"

Angi looked puzzled, so he expanded. "Jan's father and I lost track of him during a skirmish. We both thought he was dead—never saw him again until I got off the landing boat here and saw him giving orders. You can bet that was a shock."

"You don't know what happened from then till now?"

Sabine shook his head. "No, and I don't intend to ask him and blow my cover. I'll expect you to keep my secret; anyone who fought on either side at Hallam is still a pariah."

"Of course."

"In a war, people think and act differently than they do otherwise. There isn't much time for affection. I liked Jan well enough as a boy, but I never felt toward him like I do toward you. We just didn't have time for the softer emotions.

"Still, I liked him. He was a brave, decent boy and he has grown into a brave, decent man. But there is some demon riding him. You'd best find out what that demon is before you marry him."

He hesitated so long that Angi thought he had finished. Both of them were staring across the courtyard to where Jan was dressing down a careless archer. "Another thing for you to think about. Daniel Andrax, Jan's father, was a driving, self-assured man—a born leader. He had a faith in himself and his religion that would stop at nothing.

"He was a lot like your father—and you can bet that Jan has seen the resemblance, too."

26

Marcel Dumezil, patriarch of the Benedictine Monists on the planet called Harmony, moved with assurance in everything he did. It was not egotism, exactly, that made him feel his every act was correct, but faith in God, faith in his special place in God's plan, and faith in his understanding of that plan. Had he been accused of egotism, he would have denied the charges hotly—but humbly. He had long since transcended identifying his personal wishes with God's. Now he was tangled in the less common, but more dangerous fallacy of identifying God's personal wishes as his own.

Marcel Dumezil was a man without doubts. He was also a man of great practical wisdom and vast experience in colonizing and in the leading of colonists. He held himself to be indispensable and was more than half right.

He slept only four hours each night, devoting to prayer the other four hours he allowed himself away from his duties. Hypocrisy was not one of his characteristics; he believed utterly in his God and his mission. And this made him dangerous. Lacking internal weakness, he tolerated no weakness in his followers. Believing first in God and only secondarily in man, he was utterly ruthless.

He had thrown the grenade.

The herds came. Like an endless river they flowed past the palisade. The colonists worked themselves into exhaustion with the slaughter, killing, killing, killing; butchering until their skins ran red with blood, until their hair was matted with clotted, black, insect-ridden blood. Haunch after haunch of trihorn, herby, humpox, and leer tumbled into the pit north of town to be covered with clean sand and still more haunches. Bones and entrails inundated the land.

On the third day of the hunt, the skimmer was destroyed by a moving mass of flesh. Tennyson Risley had been piloting it between the hunters and the pit. Broken castings and twisted sheet metal were scattered over a square kilometer and Tenn's body was lost to

27

the scavengers along with the load of meat he had been carrying.

On the eighth day of the hunt, young Jean Dumezil, the patriarch's third son, was carried in dead, his throat ripped out by a longneck. He was wrapped in the skin of the animal which had killed him and buried beside Tom Dennison and Jason D'Angelo. Marcel Dumezil read the service dry-eyed.

Walking away from the grave, Lucien Dubois and Alexandre Chambard could not meet one another's eyes. They remembered the day they had found young Jean standing over the body of Jason D'Angelo, a bloody club in his hand. They remembered all too well how Jean had felt no contrition for the murder, reminding them how D'Angelo had mocked their God.

They remembered dragging the body to a place where it would be struck by a falling tree. They remembered the look on Jan Andrax's face when he found tiny bits of moss embedded in the wound.

And Lucien Dubois remembered Jason's near-death protecting him from a charging leer.

When the herds had left, the land was tortured, gouged, and mangled. It was a morass of drying dung, blood, entrails, and bones.

The herbivores had swept the ground like locusts, leaving nothing behind. All plant life was gone and within a week the moisture was gone as well; the land stretched away as pure desert, save for the trees on the mountains behind the camp and the tough new growth that sprang up near the shrunken river.

A week after the herds' disappearance, Helene Dumezil and Valikili were married. The ceremony took place in the courtyard, attended by the entire colony. Angi squeezed Jan's arm in delight at its conclusion, a delight that died when she saw the look in his eyes. It was the look of a caged animal.

28

Chapter 5

The camp had fallen into a pitiful squalor. The palisade was far too small and the brush huts inside were not only pathetic shelters but also a grave fire hazard. One spark could wipe them out.

The time had come to expand the colony and to go down to the lake, a distance of 450 kilometers and one the colonists were reluctant to make. They had been living from moment to moment for five months and wanted some time to rest and enjoy the fruits of their labor. Once again, Jan was thankful for Marcel Dumezil's drive. The leader agreed that the colony must move and must expand.

The colony needed a constant supply of fresh water. The river Lydia was too seasonal in its flow to support proper sanitary facilities, though it provided enough water for their primitive life style. The lake would allow a nonseasonal access to protein—fish—and a chance to try domesticating the native plants. Jan was convinced that water was the limiting factor in plant growth and that irrigation could provide a bountiful harvest of native flora.

The patriarch agreed with him on every particular. They spent a month finalizing plans for the new "city" —a trying time for Jan as he fought against his natural dislike of the man.

Captain Childe confirmed Jan's suspicions; the melt would come twice yearly but the herds only accompanied one melt. When the green latitude moved northward, the herds would follow the opposite shore of the lake.

For two months the land was desert, then for four months it was snowy. Throughout that time the colonists cut logs until great rafts of timber awaited the melt. They would form the palisade of the new lower colony. The women smoked meat and prepared pemmican.

The *Lydia* was now in a stationary equatorial orbit just overhead. Captain Childe had only to request it and Henri Staal would take the landing craft up to get him, but he persisted in his self-imposed exile. He had converted holdspace to hydroponic tanks using algae native to Harmony and had established a closed-cycle ecosystem for himself. Jan was sure that he had no intention of ever grounding.

Jan was on the crew that went to the lake. They steered their rafts into the shallows at the height of the flood and drove in the long pilings they had prepared. Then they sat, imprisoned on their wooden islands, living on raw fish to preserve their pemmican, and waiting for the melt to pass. When the waters had receded, they surveyed a site on a bluff on the south bank of the Lydia. There they dug trenches and carried up the logs.

Everything they had cut in six months was used to make the stockade. Houses would wait until the next melt. The return trip was made afoot, staying near the Lydia for her failing, muddy water.

Two more couples were married within a week of their return.

Angi rolled over and leaned on one elbow. The faint light touched one bare breast until she rearranged her clothing. Even in lovemaking they could not undress fully and for that Jan damned the cold planet anew.

"When are you going to marry me, Jan. I'm getting tired of snatching love when we can find a hole to hide in."

He sat up and adjusted the hang of his pistol. It was true, more for him than for her. He could never relax and enjoy their brief liaisons because his Scout training kept him looking for danger when he should be concentrating on her; furthermore, he felt guilty for breaking his own rules about going beyond the sentry line.

But what could he say? "Hon, it isn't as simple as it seems."

"Why isn't it?"

To that he didn't reply.

"You owe me the truth."

"Not really. It may be that I owe you silence."

"No, Jan." He looked around uneasily and she smiled. He was worried about longnecks and afraid that if he suggested that they leave she would think he was avoiding the question. And at the same time, he *was* avoiding it. "Tell me about Hallam."

She could not have shocked him more if she had shot him.

"How did you know about that!"

"No, I'm sworn to secrecy on my source. But I deserve to know—and I need to know—why you hate and fear my people."

When he didn't reply, she said, "Jan, either you let me into your life or I'll put you out of mine."

He dropped an oath. "Sexual blackmail?"

"No. Self-preservation. You know me better every day, but to me you remain an enigma. I can't live with that."

He cursed again and drew his weapon. It was apparent that there would be no retreating behind the sentry line now and defense remained his first instinct. "You won't like the story."

"No, I'm sure I won't."

Chapter 6

Interlude: Incident on Hallam's World

"Andrax, you can't seriously contend that crucifixion is a viable part of the Monomythos. It is a barbaric concept, not a true part of the Word." The speaker was angry, as was my father's reply.

"It is not my place to advise God on what is and is not proper. Crucifixion, the self-sacrifice of God for Man, is a part of a vast array of religions from Zulis to the Christ. Who are we to throw it out?"

They stood face to face, poised like fighting cocks, two small men with pretensions to power, each secure in his own theology. This I know now, but then I only saw that my father was threatened by the heretic Baylor and that, insofar as he was threatened, I was likewise threatened. I was twelve years old.

I remember the incident clearly still. It was the last argument that Baylor and my father had. I had been schooled in the Danneline Monomythos and I believed it implicitly. There was no room for doubt in my small, ordered world.

The sun was warm; flowers were blooming in the village square on the imported fruit trees that were our village's special pride. The grass was green after a long winter of brown and the pond at the base of the muddy main street was clear blue again, having shed its winter coat of ice. All these details are made more poignant by the intervening years and the comparison they offer to this cold hell-planet. Hallam, or Hallam's World as it is often called, is a prime property.

A crowd gathered as the argument continued, each man gesturing with the staff he carried to kill the poisonous reptiles then prevalent. Baylor's supporters were almost exclusively newcomers to Hallam, the company of a ship that had planeted only two years back. They were followers of the Pertoskan Monomythos, demons to me then. Now I recognize that the difference in doctrine between their people and mine was small.

When Louis Dumezil collated the earth's religions into one grand scheme, he had hoped to put an end to religious persecution by deriving a universal religion. Scholars are uncertain today whether or not he believed in his teachings himself; it is a common theory among historians that he was not a religious man, merely a man of peace working through religion to attain his ends. If that is so, he failed miserably, for there has never been a more fractious group than the Universal Monists.

By the time the argument had continued for ten minutes, most of the village had gathered, each group of adherents separating from the other. My father was red-faced; Baylor had gone white. Each was gesturing, shouting, cutting off his opponent, making personal slurs. Then Baylor struck my father—or my father struck Baylor. I have never been quite sure who struck the first blow, nor are my impressions of the melee that followed clear. In seconds the entire village was engaged in a general brawl. I rushed to my father's aid and was promptly smashed down, whether by friend or foe I am not sure. He and Baylor stood toe to toe trading blows with their staves until Baylor fell. I remember staggering to my feet and being caught up in my father's arms as he retreated with me.

He dropped me to the dirt floor inside our house, and I sat holding my head while he and my mother argued. He was rummaging in his chest, that same chest he had carried two decades earlier when he emigrated. I could make little sense of my mother's words for she was hysterical. I stood, swayed, leaned against a table and watched as my father pulled out the automatic pistol he had taken as plunder in some war. He checked its load, drew back the cocking bar and strode out. I can see his face as if it were before me and even now, as then, the expression is unreadable.

He left the house at a run and I heard the bullroar of a heavy rifle. My father was not the only one to have gone for better weapons. Then I heard a scream and it went on and on, high-pitched, mad, the cry of a woman bereaved. More shots echoed, different pitches distinguishing different weapons, some of which I recognized. I heard more screams as I staggered outside. Buildings intervened between me and the fighting, but I could see flames where someone's house was burning. My mother caught my arm and held me back.

The flames had spread to other buildings, or were being spread. Alan crouched beside my mother; he was ten. I realized that Jennie was not with us. Someone ran up our street, staggered, and fell. Then he began to crawl forward, and when he raised his head I recognized him. Mr. Thoms! I broke away and ran to him. He had been shot through the leg and was bleeding badly. I stopped the wound and helped him drag himself inside the house. Wounds were nothing new to me, even then, for Hallam was still a frontier world.

His face was white from shock and loss of blood. "Anna," he said, gripping my mother's arm, "it's terrible. Those damned new people . . ." He broke off, too angry to continue. The smell of smoke had reached us now. Firing was sporadic, but unrelenting. Apparently both sides had taken cover to snipe at one another. Two women herded a group of children into sight, heading toward us. Our house was one of the town's original structures, of full hewn logs set on a mound with an open field of fire, a relic of first ship days when the cannys had not yet been killed off. It was apparent that they intended to take shelter here. I took down *Papa's* single-shot hunting rifle and loaded it, cursing myself for not having remembered it sooner, and went down to help.

The women were Mrs. Thoms and her daughter Margaret, but the children were a mixed lot, her own and a round dozen from other families. She saw her man as she entered the house and ran to him with tears of relief on her face. Margaret was all dry-eyed business, herding the children to an inner room and threatening dire punishment if they whimpered or left its security. Then she came back and walked to where *Mama* and Alan were crouched. Her face was white; she seemed in greater shock than her father, though there was no wound on her. She looked down at *Mama* and said, "I saw Jennie. She's dead."

It was a flat pronouncement, with no more emotion than a discussion of the weather. At first it didn't sink in, then *Mama* began to cry, open-eyed, open-mouthed, a mad, rising sound. I shut it out, shut out my sister's memory, and fled down toward the fighting.

I rounded the corner and looked out across the village square, keeping down. Bodies littered the ground. Some were twisted grotesquely or bore visible wounds. Those I could accept. It was the ones who lay quietly as if in repose, their wounds hidden, that bothered me most. I knew them all, first-shippers and newcomers alike, both Dannelites and Pertoskans.

A group of men leaped up and charged my position. I swung *Papa's* gun around, then recognized *Papa* in the lead. Dust danced near their feet and I swung back toward the snipers, fired, hit nothing. They broke over me and took cover behind the same overturned cart I had sheltered in.

Papa's face was smeared and bloody. He spared me only one comment, "Reload, dammit!" Shocked back to attention, I did so.

We waited behind the cart. Occasionally one of us or one of them tried a shot, most of which went wild. One of theirs burned Sabine Conners's shoulder. Probably we did no more damage than that.

After a while my father turned to me and asked, "Are your mother and the children safe?"

"Mother and Alan are at the house."

"Where's Jennie?"

I gestured, "Out there . . . dead."

For a moment he said nothing, then he leaped up

and fired, releasing rounds in a single roar of sound until his automatic was empty. He screamed. Three shots came from the enemy; two missed. The third hit the cart just before *Papa* and exploded a board into a hundred splinters, all of which hit him. He went down, cursing and bleeding wildly. Sabine and I were on him in a moment, but his wounds, though numerous, were superficial. We caught him up and retreated to the house.

Damn this cold planet for dredging up memories. Still, I could probably have forgiven, could probably react to these people around me as people, not simply as Monists, if there were no sequel to the memory. But in the end it is not what happens *to* us, but what we do ourselves, that affects us most.

Daniel Andrax, my father, came to Hallam's World on the first ship, worked hard, built a place for himself and his family, and aided in the building of the community. He proposed and largely supported the drive to raise money for the importation of fruit trees. He fought cannys—deadly, persistent predators—and was in the forefront of the drive to bring in the dogs that finally finished them off.

Daniel Andrax was a deeply religious man, a Danneline Monist and a minister of that faith. He was a brilliant leader, both religious and secular, a good provider, and a good father. He was also a zealot with little time for opinions other than his own, but that is not an uncommon failing.

He was not unlike Marcel Dumezil.

A decade after Hallam's World was settled, the second shipload of colonists arrived. Natural increase had already doubled the population of the original colony. For the Ministers of Colonization this is the prime index of success, and in the next decade twelve more colony ships arrived. In the influx Daniel Andrax could have easily lost his preeminence, but he did not.

A conflict based on the doctrinal differences between the two Monist denominations did develop, and

Baylor became the Pertoskan champion. It has been suggested that all of the warfare between the two sects was a result of political pretensions given the guise of a holy war. This is not true. I knew my father better than anyone, both then and later; he was a truly religious man in both the best and worst senses of the word. He felt that the search for God's word among the complex and contradictory lessons of the "Great Religions of Earth" was a holy task, one that had been concluded correctly, once and for all time, in the Danneline Monomythos. He would not abide attacks upon it, or Baylor's attempts to have his version of the Monomythos elevated to official status. That their secular pretensions also clashed was a strictly secondary consideration.

When the war broke out there were eleven thousand colonists on Hallam, about a thousand of them living in a cluster of villages called Hallam, which was also the capital "city" and starport. There Baylor and my father fought as they returned from services in their respective churches. By that night the entire town was fighting and half of it ablaze.

We abandoned our post that night and took to the hills. Most of the first-shippers had been Dannelites and the Pertoskans who came later were of a different breed that had gravitated to the towns. In Hallam City we were outnumbered three to one. In fact, my father had threatened to abandon the house and move into the outback for years; only his politicking had kept him tied to the place.

Hallam was set on the floodplain of a minor river near its mouth and backed by a rugged coastal mountain range. We eased out of the house some hours before dawn and were at the base of the mountains by sunrise. There was no pursuit.

We began a guerrilla war, slipping down from the mountains to raid, pillage, and burn. I went on my first raid within a month of the outbreak of hostilities. *Papa,* Mr. Thoms, and Sabine Conners slipped down to a Pertoskan farm in hopes of stealing burros. I remained with *Papa*'s automatic pistol on a hillock over-looking the house; I was to lay down covering fire should they be spotted. No one actually expected me to hit anybody, just to keep their heads down.

They were waiting for us; how they knew that we were coming I never did find out. As our men approached the corrals, the Pertoskans fired from ambush. All three went down. I was so startled by the suddenness and shaken by the roar of gunfire that I forgot to fire. Then one of the Pertoskans stood up, laughing, and I shot him three times. He crumpled like a ragdoll.

Then there was only silence.

Several minutes later I saw movement in the bushes outside the Pertoskan house and emptied the rest of the clip. Somebody screamed. I reloaded and waited.

After ten minutes the bushes below me rustled. I covered the area and waited until *Papa*'s voice reached me. He was dragging Sabine Conners; Mr. Thoms was dead.

That was the beginning.

Any boy on the frontier becomes an efficient woodsman and is tough in mind and body. At twelve I had drawn blood, though I am no longer proud of that achievement. In the months that followed I became a hardened and highly efficient guerilla. My size allowed me to slip into places a grown man would not have dared, and the revolver I captured some weeks into our exile made me as deadly as any adult. What my father thought of the changes in me, I did not know. As always he was aloof, brooding now about the loss of his lands, his position, and his daughter.

In those days *Papa* was often tied up with matters of administration. We made our headquarters in a cluster of log houses we took in a high valley. Every day more Dannelites straggled in, each influx fanning our angers with new tales of terror. That we also spread terror was my pride; only later could I see the whole affair in perspective.

Even when *Papa* could not go, Sabine and I went raiding. We stole stock and food, clothing, arms and

38

ammunition, and sometimes we found ourselves in firefights. I watched men go down before my gun and heard them scream from cover. Many of the former were probably just wounded and some of the latter probably died. It was impossible to assess our successes and failures.

We survived.

Somehow the Pertoskans manage to maintain secrecy about our war. Then as now, there is no fast long-range communication except by ship. Synapse technology can send solid bodies but not messages. For a year we had the field to ourselves and mercilessly slaughtered each other for the glory of God, but eventually a ship landed and carried away rumors of rebels in the hills. The Patrol ship that investigated found more than rebels and returned for reinforcements.

When the Patrol peacekeeping force arrived I was a seasoned veteran of thirteen. The Pertoskans were subdued at once since they were tied to the towns. We simply changed enemies and kept on fighting.

More time passed and we were severely pressed, forced out of the foothills and into the high mountains. Food was scarce and ammunition could no longer be had at all when our scouts brought word of a detachment moving into our area. We laid an ambush.

They came up through a long valley and turned toward our camp, cutting through the narrow ravine where we were poised. They had two civilian scouts, Pertoskans, ordered to duty but relishing a chance to take their revenge on us. We let them come until they were directly below us and opened fire. The Pertoskans went down together and the Patrol went to earth like the trained soldiers they were, leaving three of their number behind.

We waited then, having a commanding position, and kept them pinned down. The light duty half-track growled forward and to the left until it jammed between two trees, its driver slumped over the controls. Sabine and I slipped down to recover the supplies it carried.

We were fools. We should never have stayed there

after our first burst of fire, but we were unused to fighting a modern force. Sabine and I worked our way down, taking our time, and were sorting through the half-track's contents when we heard a strange humming. Sabine knew immediately what we were facing. He hit the bushes, shouting for me to follow, but I turned to see what was coming.

It was a silver bullet, whizzing across the treetops at a hundred kilometers an hour, ducted fans thrusting down the air which supported it, flattening the vegetation as it went. For an almost fatal moment I paused, then leaped for cover. A high-explosive shell hit the spot where I had been standing. Everything went black.

And was black when I woke, but of a different kind. I felt suffocated and found myself bound. For a moment I panicked, then lucidity returned and I explored my bonds. Only I wasn't bound as I had thought; rather my torso was encased in a hard plastic shell, either bandages or a cast—or both. I stood up, supported myself until the first dizziness had passed, then explored in the darkness. I had been lying on a pallet in a room no larger than a closet with cold, metallic walls and one door. There were no windows and no other facilities. After a while I lay down again and slept.

Light wakened me again and two men entered my cubicle. The elder seemed kindly enough, but his young, armed companion had the look of hate. Had he been alone I do not think I would have fared well.

"How do you feel?" the elder asked.

I shrugged. He ignored my reticence and took my pulse, then passed over me with a medical sensor, so I concluded he was a doctor. "What happened to me?"

"You were struck by the blast from an explosive and cracked three ribs, presumably when you hit the ground. This," he tapped the plastic corset, "is a cast. In a month you will never know you were hurt." He turned to his companion, "Conduct him to the head, then bring him back here, and provide food and water."

After that the lights cycled on and off at regular intervals which corresponded to the day outside. I was fed, watered, doctored, and ignored for four days. On the fifth day I was escorted to an office and left there to face a Patrol officer.

I seated myself and said nothing. Let the soldier make the first move. He was somewhat older than my father, with the first hints of gray in his hair. He stared at me a long time before speaking.

"How old are you, son?"

"Old enough."

"No doubt. How old is old enough?"

"Thirteen."

He nodded and made a job of lighting his pipe. "What's your name?" I said nothing. "You are Jan Andrax, son of Daniel Andrax, are you not?" Again I said nothing. "We had some local people identify you while you were still unconscious, you see. We would like to get your cooperation, in hopes of ending this pointless war. Your father can stay up in those hills and continue to wreak havoc for quite some time. I won't lie to you, son; our job isn't easy. But we will win. Eventually, we will win."

I spat on his rug. Anger flared on his face but he controlled it. "If you will help us, we can save many lives, not only Pertoskan but your people's as well. It's time for your father to stop fighting a losing battle."

Then we were both silent and he merely stared at me. For a few moments I matched his stare, then turned away, shamed by my weakness.

"Damn!" It seemed as if he were talking to himself, not me. "How can they do this to one so young?"

"I'm old enough to make you bastards bleed!"

"Yes, you certainly are. And inordinately proud of the fact." He leaned forward, "Son—"

"I'm not your son!"

"No!" He struck the table with his fist. "No, you aren't, dammit. My son was killed in that ambush."

"Good!" He came around the desk with speed

amazing for a man so heavy and struck me down before I could dodge.

Three days later a steel collar with attached chain was riveted around my neck and I was led out and padlocked to the dashboard of a personal skimmer. The officer who had interrogated me sat beside me and two privates sat forward, one piloting, one manning the machine rifle. What the officer had in mind, I could not guess.

We toured the valley where the Patrol base was situated, and I saw the blackened ruins we had made of once prosperous farms. I exulted in the destruction. It was not more than the Pertoskans deserved for driving us from our lands and killing off my sister and my friends.

The officer said nothing until the end of the tour, then asked, "Are you proud of what your people have done."

"Yes!"

Thereafter, hardly a day passed that I was not escorted somewhere to view the destruction we Dannelites were perpetrating. I worked beside a Pertoskan whose house had been burned. For a week I labored with him to rebuild it, thinking all the while that if I escaped I would return and burn it again. Whenever a Pertoskan was killed, I dug the grave, wrapped the body, and watched the mourners as they trooped past. I spaded the dirt back into the grave.

At first I was proud of the destruction; then I reached a stage wherein I could no longer be proud, though I still accepted the destruction as necessary to free Hallam. After a while, it became apparent that Hallam would never again be a Dannelite paradise and I took solace in revenge.

After months of uncounted bodies, burned fields, and destroyed homes, I no longer wanted revenge. I had become numb.

At night I was locked away in the tiny cubicle. It

was not imprisonment or punishment—it was to keep the Pertoskans from reaching the son of their persecutor.

Whenever a new raid occurred, I rode with Major Bass, my personal demon, to view the carnage. My pride lasted for two such missions. Thereafter I was merely dumb and resentful, moving as directed, bundling up the shattered bodies to be taken down to the valley for burial.

Sometimes we would sweep up the valleys on a skimmer and Bass would question me on this topic or that, trying to wring tactical information out of me. In this he was not successful.

On one such mission he turned to me and asked, "Do you think me cruel in my treatment of you?" When I did not answer, he went on, "Remember this, Jan; when your father stops butchering innocent people, you will no longer have to bury them."

In my cell that night, I found a new addition to his arsenal of tortures. A technician had set up a reader so that it ran continuous spools of the Pertoskan and Danneline Monomythoses side by side. At first I ignored it, since it was cased in clear plastic and I could do it no harm. Then I thought that I would fool him by reading only the scriptures that had been my companions since infancy and deriving comfort from them. For two hours I read until something seemed wrong. The scriptures suddenly took a new slant and I realized that they had become foreign to me. I glanced at the parallel tape and realized that I had been fooled. The labels had been reversed. For two hours I had been reading the Pertoskan Monomythos and had not known the difference.

I resolved to read neither thereafter, but the fascination of the flittering words in an otherwise barren room drew me back. For three days no one came near except to feed me and at the end of that time I had read both Monomythoses twice and realized for the first time how tiny were the differences between them.

We went on patrol then as we had done so many times before. I had been a prisoner five months by that

43

time and my fourteenth birthday had come and gone. The first night we stopped at an isolated farmhouse. Major Bass tried to persuade the man and his wife to leave for the valley, warning of the danger from Dannelite raiders, but he would not go. It was his land, the man said, and no one could take it from him.

He had two daughters, one about the age Jennie would have been, sixteen or perhaps a year older, and the other about six. As I sat chained to a tree, apart from the family and the soldiers, the younger approached in shy wonderment.

"Why are you chained?" I did not reply, for I had cultivated silence as the only answer due to Bass and his allies. "What did you do?"

"Nothing."

"Nothing? Then why are you tied up?" She turned to her sister who was approaching, "Anne, why is this man tied up? He didn't do anything."

The elder sister pulled her back. "Yes, he did, Honey; he's the son of the man who leads the Dannelites."

"Is that any reason to treat him like a dog and tie him up?"

The question seemed to trouble the older sister, and, somewhat puzzled, she looked at me. "Now, Honey, he isn't just the son of that man. He was a raider himself. He raided houses like ours and killed people like Daddy and Mummy."

The younger sister turned to me, big-eyed and unbelieving. "Did you really do that, mister?"

I opened my mouth to say, "No," then closed it again and turned away.

Later, when the soldiers had eaten and had given me my ration of dried meat, the girls returned with a bowl of fresh milk. The elder sister held little Honey back and extended the bowl to me, carefully not coming within reach. I took it and drank gratefully, but her reticence burned me. "What do you think I'm going to do, pull you down and strangle you on the spot?"

She squatted on her heels and watched me drink.

44

"Maybe. Maybe not, but maybe. How am I to know what you are capable of doing? Some of your kind have done worse."

"Then why give me this milk?"

She gestured toward Honey, squatting big-eyed some distance away. "Because I want her to learn kindness."

Two days later we returned to the farm after an unsuccessful scouting mission. The barns and house were gone, leaving only ash and embers to mark their passing. The man who had refused to leave his land lay sprawled in the yard. His wife lay in the doorway of the house, so badly burned as to be unrecognizable. The soldiers fanned out searching for the daughters.

Major Bass came to where I was tethered, his face more pale and angry than was usual, and dragged me along behind him. They lay beyond the bushes where the grass and flowers made a soft bed. Honey was crumpled, her back stained with dried, blackened blood. Anne lay beyond. She was dead. She was naked. She had been raped.

I dropped to my knees, tears streaming down my cheeks. Now I would have to wrap those two pitiful bodies and load them. Later I would prepare them for burial. I would dig the grave; I would throw the dirt upon them.

Major Bass's hand was on my shoulder then and he drew me away from that haunted place. Some of his soldiers took the bodies away.

That night they struck the collar from my neck and the next morning Major Bass saw me in his office. I had not been there since the fifth day of my capture.

"I'm sending you offworld with the next supply ship."

I was not surprised. "To a prison planet?"

He waved the notion aside. "Of course not. The Federation does not punish children for being their father's sons. You will be sent to Aleph base for schooling."

I said nothing, ready for a trap.

"You don't believe me, do you?"

"What price is this favor? Are you trying to bribe me into betraying my father?"

He went to the map that covered one wall of his office and pointed directly to our home base. "Two weeks ago we raided here. Your father escaped with some of his men, but they are in entirely new territory now. There is nothing you could tell us of importance, even if you were willing to do so."

"I am not."

"I would hope that you are not. I respect loyalty."

"Why then, damn you! Why have you punished me these last months if not to break my spirit—to get me to tell what I know."

He took a long time answering. "When you came to me, my son had just been killed. Had you been an adult, I would probably have executed you. I, too, am not immune to revenge. But your youth made me think of my own son and what he might have become in your place. In memory of him I decided to see if there was a man worth salvaging under that fanatic's shell. I was right; there was such a man. Had you been older, my tactics would not have worked.

"You have not been under punishment—I have been educating you."

Jan never came to like Major Bass, nor did Bass ever come to like Jan, but their strange relationship persisted and they came to respect one another. When Bass rose to colonel, he suported Jan's bid for Scout training. Had he not pulled strings, Jan's background would have kept him out of Federation service. For that Jan owed him fully as much as for his harsh education on Hallam.

Why could he not marry Angi? Put simply—fear. Fear for what the future held for them both. No one can fully gauge the depths of fanaticism who has not been a fanatic himself.

Chapter 7

When the third melt came, the colonists moved to the lake. It had taken all of the patriarch's powers of persuasion to force the move and still they were reluctant. Four barges had been built and several huge rafts of logs. The women and belongings went in the former with a portion of the men while the remainder of the men guided the rafts down and beached them near the palisade. All this was done early in the melt, and when the herds came in earnest the men had already dragged the now empty barges back upstream to hunt the year's meat supply.

Three weeks later the hunt was completed and the meat stored away in a new permafrost cellar. Then one group of the colonists began to construct permanent dwellings within the stockade from the timber rafts, while another began the back-breaking excavation of irrigation canals for a farm. Seeds were ready at hand, lying dormant in the dessicated soil, waiting for the next melt. River water rushed in some weeks later to provide an artificial melt. Jan's point proved, the colonists worked in earnest thereafter, digging irrigation ditches against the next melt.

The snow came, bringing a halt to the digging, and the entire colony turned to the production of shelters. Like the upper colony's, the first shelters at the lake were crude, but one substantial building was erected, a combination city hall and worship house. In the coming years the crude shelters would be replaced with solid homes.

Three months after the melt, Jan, Henri Staal, and Nur Mohammet hiked to the upper colony with a timber-cutting crew, then took the landing boat up to the *Lydia*.

Captain Childe met them with tears in his eyes. He had not seen another human face for more than a year, but he refused their entreaties that he descend to the planet. They toured the ship with him, marveling at the hydroponic setup he had built to sustain his life and noted the futile efforts he still made to repair the computer.

"You see," he said, "I have rebuilt the logic unit of the navigation section. We may not know where we are, since the memory banks were destroyed, but we can leave here now to search out a better planet or merely to explore."

Jan could not answer the captain, not having known him well, so it was Henri Staal who convinced the man that the colonists would never leave their new home.

They stayed a week, though their mission could have been accomplished in half that time. When they left, they carried makeshift nuclear devices jury rigged from the by-products of the *Lydia*'s drive unit. They landed at the passes north of the lower colony and blasted them shut, cutting off the herds from the plains near the lake where the colonists would establish their farms. Then they lifted off one last time in a shallow flight that landed them near the lower colony.

That night Henri Staal radioed to the *Lydia* and told Captain Childe of their success.

"Henri," Childe asked, "are you content to stay there? If you had the choice of going with me in the *Lydia* to explore would you do so or would you stay where you are?"

"Why, stay, of course. What is the point of exploration now. We could not relay what we found to the Federation and it will be many generations before we even explore and populate this planet."

"Don't you feel the need to explore for its own sake?"

"Perhaps I did once, but no more."

After they had signed off, Henri stepped out of the

landing boat and looked up to where the *Lydia* hung in orbit. Sudden fire lanced the heavens. Staal stood transfixed, then ran back up the ramp and tried to raise the *Lydia,* but there was no response.

When he went outside again the heavens were empty. *Lydia* had gone exploring; Captain Childe had returned to his life's work. Someday he would die and the *Lydia* would continue on whatever course he had set for her, endlessly seeking in the loneliness of space.

Jan had warned them, but they would not listen. Only Nur, whose difference was even more outstanding than Jan's, truly believed that the crew members were in danger. Henri flatly refused to listen, pointing out that he had been fully accepted and had married. Valikili echoed his sentiments, though Jan thought he detected more than a trace of hidden worry. Valikili remembered the night he had been attacked, but that was a year past. Marcel Damle had not found a girl to marry, nor was he likely to do so. Still, Marcel had made many friends, including Anton Dumezil, the patriarch's eldest son.

Angi remained unmarried. Her relationship with Jan had cooled only slightly, though she was impatient with his refusal to marry her. He did not understand why she did not marry; certainly there were at least two dozen eligible bachelors and she could have had any one or two of them for the asking.

Sabine Conners had not revealed his identity to anyone but Angi. He was not convinced that Jan was imagining things; he, too, remembered Hallam's World.

Jan made his warnings and remained ready for what he feared to be inevitable, but the day it came he was caught unprepared. The entire colony, save Nur Mohammet, had gathered for the Sabbath service in the town hall and the patriarch rose to deliver his message. He eyed the crowd in silence for a moment, then said, "We are not all present.

49

"There is one among us who does not bow his head to the will of God. He openly defies the Maker by refusing to attend His services and persists in praying to a false God.

"We cannot tolerate his presence any longer.

"Nor can we tolerate those who sit among us, but are not with us in the spirit . . ."

Jan felt Dumezil's eyes on him. His muscles tightened, readying for any action that might be needed. His eyes flitted here and there, weighing possibilities. Marcel Damle looked scared but was trying to remain inconspicuous. Henri was holding Marie's hand possessively, as if unwilling to let anything separate them. Sweat stood out on Valikili's dark face.

"The time has come for a reckoning. God saw fit to separate us from the rest of the human race, to bring us here to this place, to let us make what we will of it. It is a cold world, and harsh. Was it God's will to hurl us into torment? No! It was a testing. We have stood firm in our faith and we have conquered. Yet that is not enough. Did God cast us into this place for no purpose? You know He did not. He separated us from the heathen portion of our race to purify us and make us whole before him. We have an entire planet set before us, a barren, inhospitable planet which we can make over into a new Eden. And God will show the way toward the making of a new Eden. He will be with us.

"But only . . . only . . .

"Only if we first purify ourselves in His sight. Who is with God?"

They shouted in unison. Jan tried to shout, for self-preservation, but the cry stuck in his throat.

"Who is with Him?"

They shouted again.

"Who will purify themselves before Him?"

Jan knew what was coming.

"Who will take a hand to purify God's community?"

Jan looked left and right while rising to his feet with the congregation. There were two persons between him and the aisle and somewhere outside Nur

50

Mohammet sat in ignorance, not knowing that he was marked for death.

"Who will stand with God? Who will cast out the wicked?"

Jan moved, shouting, "I will!" He shoved past the two on his left and reached the aisle. Dumezil was dumbfounded by Jan's action; he stopped in mid-sentence.

Then Jan bolted for the door.

Two burly colonists had been posted to stop him. Jan had refused the patriarch's order to surrender his express pistol to the colony's armory and was never without it. He wore it now, but strapped to his thigh inside his trousers. He had not dared to wear it openly to the services.

Still he was a Scout, and therefore a master of weaponless combat. He caught one colonist's outstretched arm and hurled him down the aisle, then downed the second with a blow to the throat. A hand fell on his shoulder and spun him around. The whole congregation was on its feet and coming for him. Someone dodged past him, trying to get behind him. Jan recognized him as Adrian Dumezil, but could not reach him for fighting off those before him.

But Adrian did not attack him from behind; instead he threw open the door of the meeting house and Jan spun in instant retreat. Adrian pounded at his side.

Damle, Staal, and Valikili were in desperate danger but there was nothing Jan could do for them now. Nur would be in his own house, reading the Koran as was his custom.

As he ran, Jan ripped open his trousers and fished out his express pistol. The colonists were on his heels as he rounded the corner of Nur's street. He fired a maximum charge at the wall of Nur's dwelling, aiming high. It struck a log and exploded in a burst of bark and splinters. Jan and Adrian ran side by side, the colonists behind them, as Nur burst out of his house to see what was wrong.

More than anyone, Nur was prepared for what had happened. He took it all in at a glance and ran.

The main gate was closed and barred. Jan fired over Nur's head repeatedly, each shot a maximum charge, until the gate gave way, falling outward in a cloud of debris. The trio ran through the gap and down toward the river where Jan threw himself behind a slight rise along the bank and dialed the power down. The colonists were streaming out the gate and he shot repeatedly into their packed mass. They broke ranks and retreated behind the palisade.

Valikili drew Helene to one side as the crowd ran after Jan and Adrian. Marcel Damle stood just outside the town hall shaking his head in shock, muttering over and over, "They did it; they really did it." Henri Staal had run with the crowd; Valikili could not believe that he intended to join in the persecution of his shipmates and hoped that the man would not be lynched if he tried to calm the crowd.

Henri was near the back of the crowd when they poured through the palisade gate and was thrown back when they reversed themselves in the face of Jan's fire. He pulled Marie into the shadows of a nearby hut, trying to decide a course of action. The colonists were milling about while the patriarch attempted to restore order. Some had armed themselves with clubs; others had retreated to get bows and rifles. A few of the colonists were running about trying to calm their neighbors, vainly attempting to stem the madness the patriarch had started. Levi-Stuer was running from man to man, shouting for reason, tears streaming down his face, but none would hear him.

Henri started forward, then hesitated. If they would not listen to Levi-Stuer, a colonist whom they respected, what would they do to a crewman, even if he were a Monist?

What would they do to Valikili?

Horrified, he shrank back into the shadows. Something had to be done, but his wits had deserted him and he could think of no plan.

He could only think of one thing—that the madness might pass. He should have tried to help Valikili and would have but for Marie; his first duty was to his wife. He took her trembling arm and led her away from the crowd toward the south gate. They would flee to the wilderness. They could remain away from the colony and the stored food supply only so long, but in the next few days the madness might pass.

He hoped that it would, but he did not fully believe it.

Valikili was frightened for Henry Staal and cursed him for running after the colonists. Together they might have a chance to survive; divided they were in dire straits. At least Marcel Damle had remained, and Helene was close by where he could protect her.

Valikili had accepted Monism but he had not been so foolish as to assume that the Monists accepted him. He and Nur Mohammet were racially different as well as crew members. Unlike Jan he had not been schooled in small-group dynamics, but he could smell the danger in his position.

He led Marcel and Helene to his house, but paused only long enough to pick up the bundle he had prepared against such an eventuality and his bow, quiver, and blade. The rifles and ammunition were stored in "the armory," a locked closet in the town hall. If they could get them, they could hold them for a ransom of food, for without the ten offworld rifles and Jan's express pistol the colonists would be unable to hunt effectively during the coming melt. Levi-Stuer was working on a muzzle-loader Andrax had designed, but so far had completed only one unreliable prototype.

Marcel had shrugged off his shock and stolen a bow and quiver from the house next to Valikili's, while Valikili had stolen a third bow and quiver for Helene. They made their way to the armory and Valikili went to work on the door with the axe he had brought for that purpose.

The colonists had also thought of the armory and a knot of them came charging around the town hall. Valikili spun around and faced them with his axe as Marcel and Helene released their arrows. Two arrows and the crowd was upon them. Valikili laid about him

53

with the axe, his massive arms swinging in short, vicious arcs. For a moment the colonists fell back, then an arrow from the crowd struck Valikili in the thigh and he went down. Marcel stood over him with the axe he had dropped as they closed in again.

Suddenly he heard cries of fear from the colonists and they were falling back. Marcel spun to meet the new challenge behind him and found Andrax there, firing methodically. Nur, Adrian Dumezil, Henri, and Marie were behind the scout unarmed.

Valikili felt himself lifted and carried. Through the haze of his pain he saw Nur, Henri, and Marcel. Beyond them Jan Andrax stood, pistol upraised but not firing, and Marie and Adrian Dumezil were gathering blades and bows from the blood soaked ground. Helene was nowhere in sight.

Andrax had circled around the palisade with Nur and Adrian Dumezil at his heels, intending to enter the south gate to search for the rest of the crew. There they met Henri and Marie and the quintet had gone in search of their missing companions. Slipping from house to house toward Valikili's quarters, they had heard the fight at the armory and arrived just in time to see Helene being dragged back into the crowd while Marcel tried to stem what would have been a final rush. Only the superior firepower afforded by the express pistol had saved them.

Two days passed. The river gate was crudely patched. The ten offworld rifles were charged and distributed and twenty men—ten rifle-armed, ten armed with bows—stood atop the palisade.

For two days there had been no sign of the renegades, but they would return. It would be months before the melt and in all the barren desert outside the palisade there was no food. Armed parties had gone upriver, then along the shore of the lake in both directions without finding either the renegades or any trace of their presence. Of course the colonists knew that Andrax was a master of his trade; he would have covered the fugitives' tracks and there was no reason for the band to stay near water, they had merely to come down once or twice a day to drink.

But they had to have food and in all that barren waste there was none. So the colonists thought.

In fact the seven renegades were eating well enough on the dried meat that Valikili had stored against such an eventuality, nor would they have starved in any case. Along the river grew a thin fringe of siskal and lal which would have provided a meager fare; and the small, rodentlike miliks—creatures which live on the dried seedpods left behind by the herds—were available. There were few enough of these, but Jan could have trapped or shot them. In all there was enough to eat if one remained within reach of the river and stayed on the move, never exhausting the supplies of a given piece of ground.

It was fortunate for Valikili that this was not necessary, for his arrow wound, though well treated, gave him much pain. Jan had abandoned his Scout's leathers in favor of furs in order to better blend into the community, but he had not left the uniform in his quarters. He had buried it with a bow, quiver, three knives, a twenty-liter water container, some dried siskal fruit, and medical supplies judiciously stolen from the community infirmary.

Helene remained locked in her quarters, the window now sealed shut and a newly attached padlock and hasp securing the door. The patriarch had met with his closest advisors to decide her fate, but as yet they were content to use her as bait.

Two more days passed and the colonists began to wonder what would happen. No carnivores nosed about at that time of year, and only one of the renegades seemed to be injured. Where could they be? Surely their hunger would have driven them to some desperate move by then?

What if they had decided to abandon Helene Dumezil? What if Valikili had died and the others had gone upstream toward the mountains? There they would find game throughout the year, though it was never plentiful. Of course they would never make it to the mountains; they would starve on the journey.

On the fifth night Jan slipped past the sentries and found Helene. She was unhurt, she assured him through the wall, and safe enough for the moment. The patriarch had bragged to her that she was being used as bait.

Jan considered the situation. He could destroy the padlock with two shots but that would alert the guards who manned the palisade. Could he and Helene win free with the guards alerted? It was a chance he chose not to take, so he faded back into the night.

Where there was a lock, there was a key and in a colony where one man ruled with the voice of God, that man would have the key. Jan slipped his express pistol back into its holster and drew his knife.

He had not been surprised to find Helene's door unguarded, for he had already spotted the three hidden sentries who waited to pounce on anyone who came to rescue her. He had seen the same tactics used on Hallam for the same holy ends.

The guards at the patriarch's door were more obvious but harder to circumvent. Marcel Dumezil's apartment was in the second story of the town hall, with guards lounging on the catwalk before it. The two windows were shuttered and each was five meters from the ground. They would be impossible to enter—or so the guards thought.

Jan reached the roof from the rear of the building and looped a line around the chimney, then rappelled to the level of the window. He was in shadow and around the corner from the guards. As long as he remained silent, he would go undetected. He listened and was reassured by the patriarch's heavy breathing.

The shutters were latched from within but the hinges were leather and yielded instantly to his knife. He slipped inside.

Had the patriarch been a normal man, Jan could have awakened him and threatened him for the key, but the patriarch was a man of God and therefore unpredictable. He might cry out, either thinking himself invincible or valuing his life too lightly.

However, such threats would be unnecessary. On the table beside the patriarch's head was a ring of keys. In a settlement with fewer than a half-dozen locks, there was no doubt that the key he sought was on it. The task was proving too easy and Jan hesitated, then realized that he was giving his enemy credit for too much sophistication.

The patriarch slept on. Jan's knife was near at hand. It would only take one move, that yawning mouth covered to silence any outcry, and the zealot would be dead. With effective leadership gone, the purge might be ended.

A shaft of light from one of Harmony's three moons fell across old Marcel's face. Even in sleep his features showed no relaxation. A mystery Jan had all but forgotten flashed in his mind—who had thrown the grenade? Who had killed Tom Dennison, the navigator Jan had never seen in life? Who had ordered Jason D'Angelo's death; who had ordered the attack on Valikili when he kept liaison with Helene? Whose actions had prompted this situation, their flight, Helene's imprisonment, Valikili's wound?

The patriarch—Marcel Dumezil. Even those crimes he had neither committed nor ordered could be laid at his feet because of his influence.

Jan raised his knife, running his finger along the edge. He had sharpened it before the night's mission and the leather hinges had not dulled it at all. The blade would do whatever he set it to—silently and efficiently.

A vagrant breeze stirred the old man's hair, sending a wisp to tickle his nose. He snorted, stirred, then subsided.

Marcel Dumezil, colonist, organizer, leader, a man of immense talents, immense potential for good in his community—what drove him to this purge?

He was so like old Daniel Andrax.

Daniel Andrax had never been captured. He would be over fifty now—no, nearly sixty. About the same age as the patriarch. For all Jan knew he might still be hiding in the mountains of Hallam, planning raids, killing or sending out younger men to kill, still secure in his beliefs.

Jan looked down at Marcel and saw his father and, seeing him, saw himself had the roads of his life branched differently.

Lucien Dubois was guarding the house that Helene and Valikili had shared. He had one of the double rifles in his hands and was settled in the shadows a dozen meters away with a clear field of fire. He was a very unhappy man. Though he liked Valikili well enough and had known Helene since her childhood, he could not say the same for Andrax. Lucien Dubois was not a subtle man; he understood himself well enough, for his motives were simple. He wanted Angi Dumezil; he had asked her repeatedly to marry him, but she always refused. It was clear that she wanted Andrax, but he would not have her. Why that was, Dubois had never understood.

Now he waited with orders to kill anyone who might try to rescue Helene. Normally that would have been Valikili, but Val, if he lived, was sorely wounded. The rescuer would be Jan Andrax, for no other member of the renegade party was better equipped for stealth.

Lucien wanted Angi and Andrax stood in his way; yet, he did not want to kill the Scout. Dubois remembered too well his own actions in the forest above the first colony when aiding young Dumezil to cover the evidence of the murder he had committed. His hand still shook at the thought, at the guilt he had felt, at the uncertainty thereafter. Dubois would never forget the look on Andrax's face as the Scout examined Jason's body, nor would he forget the thoughtful way he examined the bits of moss embedded in the wound.

For Angi and for his own peace of mind he wanted Andrax out of the way, yet he respected the Scout. If Andrax came to rescue Helene it would be up to Lucien to kill him, but would he? Could he? Should he? Lucien loved God as much as the next man, but that didn't make the patriarch infallible.

Dubois was still debating what he might do when Jan garrotted him. His uncertainty disappeared with his consciousness.

Jan did not kill Dubois; he merely choked him into insensibility, then bound and gagged him. The Scout had already done this with the other two hidden guards, men he had hunted with, had worked and built with. Together they had raised the walls that barred the herds and made human life viable on the inhospitable planet. Andrax wished them no harm.

Still, with this last one it had been harder to release the garrote in time to let him live. Jan remembered too well Jason D'Angelo's death and was more than half convinced that Dubois, Chambard, and the dead Dumezil boy were equally responsible.

He left the rifle where it had fallen as he had the others. He could have taken them, but to do so would have jeopardized the survival of the main colony. Besides, his express pistol was worth twenty rifles.

It took only a moment to find the right key and release Helene. He had already scouted his way out and moments later a guard on the palisade fell to an unseen blow. Helene went over the palisade wall on the end of Jan's line and into the waiting arms of Marcel and Henri.

Jan did not follow her. Instead he dragged the sentry away and bound him, then retraced his footsteps. So far he had been both careful and lucky; to go back now was sheer folly.

He slit the shutter hinges of the Chambard house where Alexandre Chambard lived with his ailing wife, his three children, and Angi Dumezil, who helped with the children. Jan knew that his chances of going unheard in a household with six sleeping persons were slight, but he was determined to try.

He slipped wraithlike to the cubicle where Angi slept. It was walled off by a trihorn-hide curtain and he woke her with his hand over her mouth. She started, then relaxed, eyes wide, when she saw who it was. She put her mouth to his ear.

"What are you doing here?"

"I just broke Helene out. She is on her way to Valikili."

"Is he all right?"

"Lame but recovering."

"Oh, I'm so glad. *Papa* is mad, utterly mad."

"I know."

"How did you get her out without the key?"

"I had the key." She suddenly went stiff and he reassured her, "Your *papa* is all right. No one was badly hurt tonight."

Angi was angry. "That's more than you can say for last Sabbath. "We have eight injured and we buried three others. I hope you're proud!"

"It was forced upon us."

"You still think we're barbarians."

"I think that has been amply demonstrated."

"If only you had tried to reason with *Papa* instead of running . . ."

"Then I would be dead!"

"I don't believe it."

"You little fool, how can you say that?"

Then they were both silent, for their voices had started to raise. Finally he said, "I have to go now. Will you come with me?"

"Are you mad? You can't survive this way. Your only hope is to make peace with *Papa.*"

"Never!"

"Then go, and don't expect me to follow. When the melt comes I will put siskal flowers on your grave."

Jan jerked away and stalked to the window. Someone stirred in his sleep, but the Scout paid no heed. He climbed out the window and trotted toward the palisade, unmindful of his safety, hoping that some sentry would cross his path.

Angi lay back and slipped her hands down to her lower belly. One dry sob racked her body; then she was silent.

It was true that she did not think the renegades

could live, but her spoken refusal to follow Jan had been a lie. She would not go with him because of the thing beneath her fingers, deep in her body—the child she carried. Jan Andrax's child.

Chapter 8

For two days the party went overland, staying clear of the river. The fugitives still had some meat and Jan slipped down to refill their water bag as often as necessary, leaving no tracks to tell of his coming. Valikili walked with a makeshift crutch, Helene by his side. He was surly with pain and with shame that he had not been the one to rescue her.

Sabine Conners had discarded the name Adrian Dumezil. He told his companions that he had been on Hallam's World during the fighting and they accepted that without further questions. Fighting had no place within the renegade group.

Jan found himself looking sideways at Conners from time to time, amazed at how thoroughly the plastic surgery had changed his appearance. Sabine did not tell them he had known Jan on Hallam and Jan was content to let it stand thus.

Jan and Sabine Conners were old hands at the business of living off the land under threat of an enemy force. The others were not, but Nur and Henri were strong young men and Helene and Marie were pioneer women. They stood the trek well. Valikili suffered from his wound and slowed their flight, but he was recovering. Marcel Damle was an older man; he was doing all right while Val's wound kept the pace slow, but he would be a burden later.

The food gave out on the third day of their trek,

but they were far enough away not to fear the colonists, so they dropped down to the river, where they stripped the land as they passed, eating the few fruit pods that grew along the banks, picking the edible leaves of the greenhorn, and chewing siskal twigs for narcotic sustenance. At night they boiled siskal bark to make chota and Jan shot an occasional milik. They were eating less than their bodies were using and Jan watched with concern as their weight dropped daily.

The colonists who had to smelt iron and cut timber would be expecting them. They had taken a portable radio when leaving the lower colony months earlier and the lifeboat radio could reach them easily. Twenty men awaited them, armed with bows and two of the rifles.

On the nineteenth day they made camp below the upper colony and Jan took Sabine with him to go raiding. The other, younger men were no doubt surprised at Jan's choice of partner and Jan realized that he would have to let them know more about his past if they were to remain together.

Sabine had a bow and quiver, but would rely on his blade. Jan had observed him closely during the trek and saw that his speed and strength were only marginally diminished by age.

Three days later they returned with a heavy load of frozen meat. Jan snapped when Marie asked him what had happened and spent the afternoon in a foul temper. Later Sabine took her aside and explained that the colonists would be digging two new graves, one of them for Raoul LaBarge, a man Jan had liked and respected. Jan blamed himself for that, thinking that his approach to the fortified position had been clumsy.

They left the river and cut overland to the south. Some snow had fallen and Jan was careful to keep them to the bare rock so that they would leave no trail, though he doubted that they would be pursued. Their water gave out and they replenished it from snow. For three days they treked south-east along the foothills, then turned up a valley into the high timber.

They made camp in a high, wooded valley where

the snow was everpresent. At this altitude no true melt would occur and trees lived only because they could take their moisture directly from the snow. Jan left the others in the valley and went out to hunt alone.

He waded through the snow, at a disadvantage because he had not taken the time to make skis or snowshoes. There was much he did not know about the animals of the mountain forests. The trouble was that the planet had never been properly scouted. He himself had been acting as a colonist's advisor, something a Scout often did if he lived long enough to retire. There had been no time for exploration. Every waking minute had been aimed toward survival, toward making a viable community. Now he would have to start all over.

Before, the task of survival had been difficult; to build a community of five men and two women would be impossible. They needed more people, yet none were to be had. Even Marie seemed half ready to desert. Only her loyalty to Henri and the rough treatment Helene had received kept her from it.

Early the next morning, Jan returned with the carcass of a longneck. He had eaten longneck meat before in his initial experimentation, but the colonists had refused it, even when they killed longnecks while defending their other kills. This was a scrawny specimen with huge paws, one born for the deep snow—clearly a different variety from the herd-following longnecks.

While the steaks were broiling, Jan gathered the group together to take stock. Marie wanted to return and said so. Henri said that they could not, now that blood had been shed, and Valikili corrected that there had never been any choice since. Dumezil's sermon. Marie was unconvinced until Helene told her what Dumezil had boasted were his intentions toward the rebels.

Valikili's temper had worsened with his recovery. He was ready to wage unholy war on the colonists. Jan remained silent at the edge of the discussion until they had exhausted both bile and ideas, then told them the story of Hallam's World. He gave it to them straight, in full and gruesome detail, holding back nothing of his and Sabine's parts in the slaughter. They sat in silence through it until he finished. "So you see what will happen if we return and what will happen if we try to make war on the colonists. It would be far better if we were all to die than for that to happen."

"Then what should we do?"

"If we cannot rejoin them and we cannot raid their supplies, then we simply have to make a way for ourselves. Other rivers flow further to the south. We can settle there."

"But we have nothing with which to make a settlement."

"True."

Sabine stirred the coals with a stick and looked sidelong at Jan. "You have something up your sleeve. Out with it."

Jan stared from one face to another, wondering how his radical solution would be accepted. "Actually, I have two things up my sleeve. One—I think we went about colonizing the planet all wrong. We thought only of stable, permanent settlements with strong houses and proper fields. We harvest the melt but only in a most unaesthetic manner. We were too civilized to consider becoming nomads—following the melt."

"Impossible! We would have to walk thousands of kilometers every year."

"True, but not so many every day. It could be done."

They wrangled the idea for an hour before dropping it. Jan knew that it had taken root; he would let it simmer in their minds in the weeks to come. He had turned toward his sleeping robes when Sabine's voice stopped him. "You said that you had two things up your sleeve. You only mentioned one."

Jan looked closely at Sabine, saw the same old carelessness that had driven him on in the face of enemy fire, and was thankful for its presence. Sabine was already convinced that Jan had the only answer.

"Sabine, we cannot survive unless we augment our numbers. No group as small as ours is viable."

Sabine shrugged, "What can we do? We will find no converts among the colonists."

"Converts, no, but children . . ."

PART II

Standard Year 893 and of the colony,
Year 23

Chapter 9

Jean Dubois knelt near the icy pool and waited. Anton Dumezil was somewhere within shouting distance but likewise well hidden. The melt had been underway for a week back at the colony and they had trekked north to meet the oncoming herds; others might wait until the animals arrived nearer home but Jean and Anton were impatient in their youth. Anton was armed with one of the rifles brought in on the *Lydia*. Jean's muzzleloader had been made on Harmony by old Levi-Stuer, the gunsmith. It was probably as accurate and powerful as Anton's weapon, though slower to load, but the cartridge rifles carried an extra aura of prestige.

The wind stirred the lal bush with the soft movements of new growth. The melt is a glorious time, even as youth is a glorious time, for all the wiry, naked bushes take on flowers for a few weeks and then leaves. For a month the sun is warm (though the old ones who remembered Bordeaux complained bitterly of the cold even in high summer) and the world is green. Then the melt is gone and the vegetation with it, and the land is desert again for a season before the snows return.

The old ones complained that there were no *rain* and no *clouds,* but Jean found the idea of woolly things floating in the sky and liquid falling from it so absurd as to be unbelievable.

Across the pool the bushes stirred and Jean raised his rifle. It was a leer. They were not prized for their meat but for their skins, which were carefully removed with feathers intact. Anton had a jacket made of leer-hide which he wore on ceremonial occasions. Very impressive. The leers were always the first to come with the melt, so Jean was unlikely to get a better target. As the creature worked its way out to the pool, Jean noted with some concern that it was a male. Among leers, the female is the more deadly and they almost always run in pairs. To kill a male with a single shot rifle was to lay oneself open to attack from the female. One always shoots the female and leaves the male.

Jean relaxed his forefinger and waited, sighting past the bayonet fitted at the end of his rifle. The male dipped his head, then tipped it back to drink. Long minutes passed, but a hunter must be patient above all things. The male moved back into the bushes and Jean wondered if he had erred and thrown away his chance. Time passed.

Jean's caution was rewarded as the female strutted forth, her pink feathers iridescent in the noon sun. She was cautious. After carefully scrutinizing the area she dipped her head, then tipped it back. When her eyes were skyward, Jean shifted his aim slightly to cover the spot where she had drunk. When she dipped her head again, he fired.

The leer collapsed as the shot echoed across the pool. There was agitation in the bushes and the male burst forth.

For a space of four heartbeats Jean watched as he charged. Time seemed to hang suspended. Jean heard the insects buzzing nearby, thought of Chloe, of the warmth of the sun, and of the fabled toothless birds of other planets. He did not think of his weapons any more than he would think of his foot or his arm. They were simply there, a part of him.

The leer darted his head forward, teeth aimed at Jean's neck. A little sidestep, just as old Renou taught; the shock of contact as the teeth met on the hard leather shield at his shoulder; the shock of the bayonet going home; the shock of Jean's back striking the sodden ground as hunter and prey fell in a tangle of limbs. Then up, thrusting and parrying against that sinuous, deadly head. Finding the rifle torn from his grip. The sudden fear; the warm comfort of a blade hilt. The sudden overhand slash that ended it all.

Jean swayed on his feet, bleeding from a score of insignificant lacerations; his shoulder was bruised and painful. But the leers were dead, both of them, and he had been alone.

Anton jammed a section of leer haunch onto the stick he had sharpened, then held it to the flame. He had not made a kill during the day and he communicated his irritation through curt movements at the fire.

Jean leaned against a backrest woven from a living greenhorn and fought back a scowl. The hearts of his leers hung over the fire, but Anton had given no word of approval. Still, Anton was his friend, so he ventured, "Tomorrow your luck will change."

"You seem to have it all. Besides, I don't need luck."

Jean clamped his jaws shut and started forward, then relaxed. Anton was ready for him to make a move. Anton had always belittled him, but never before had he actually goaded him. "What's wrong with you, Anton. You act more like an enemy than a friend."

Anton sat back and something seemed to go loose inside him. He smiled with no humor. "Maybe I'm just surprised that your luck carried you through so easily."

"Like you said, luck had nothing to do with it."

Anton motioned toward the steaming hearts. "Two leers, one rifle. I call it luck."

"What's wrong with you?"

He shrugged. "Nothing. I was just surprised."

"Why? When have I ever shirked any task? Why should you expect me to fail as a hunter?"

"Oh, shut up and eat. You're just strung out from the hunt."

A week later they loaded the gig and set it free. With the melt in full swing, the North River was high, deep, and muddy. There was a stiff silence between them.

They reached the lake in three effortless days, then

spent two backbreaking ones rowing between the mouth of the North River and the mouth of the Lydia. There were half a hundred people waiting at the landing, but most of them turned away when it became apparent who they were. Those would be the relatives of the others who had gone north. Perhaps half a dozen parties of youths had gone out on advance hunts. They would bring back the first fresh meat that the colony had had in nearly a year, but that was not their true purpose in going. It was a testing of manhood, a *rite-de-passage,* though an informal one, entered into voluntarily. Such hunting was deadly dangerous and that, of course, was its appeal. The main meat harvest would come in another month when the herds crossed the Lydia.

By the time Jean and Anton had tied up, only their families and a few friends remained. Chloe was among them. They heaved up their bundles of furs and lightly salted meat. Jean's father and younger brother loaded them onto a cart.

"A very good hunt, *mon fils;* you do us proud."

"Thank you, *Papa.*"

It was good to be back, good to see Chloe again, but the edge was taken off it all by Anton's reaction. After all, he had been Jean's friend. He walked over to where Anton stood watching his uncle load his furs and meat. "A good hunt, Anton," he said, "It was a pleasure going with you."

"You did well enough, *enfant.*" Jean stiffened at the term, started to retort, then let it die. Something in Anton's eyes told him that he wanted a fight, and whatever he wanted it would serve Jean well to deny him.

Jean entered the stockade with Chloe on his arm and returned his rifle to the city arsenal. All of the original cartridge rifles were held in common trust, as were a number of Levi-Stuer's muzzleloaders. A man could rent one of the latter if he contributed a portion of his kill to the colony, but only a proven hunter could rent a cartridge rifle. It was a high privilege. Of course, one could buy a muzzleloader from Levi-

Stuer, but the price was more than it took to equip a farm. Jean, like every other youth, wanted one in the worst way.

It was Levi-Stuer's standing lament that he could not get an apprentice; the young men preferred bolder endeavors and the older men lacked the steady hands. Jean had even considered becoming his apprentice, but pride kept him from it.

They walked through the stockaded city to the river's edge. Chloe said she had missed him, called him by tender endearments she said were his alone (a declaration he tended to doubt), and they found privacy beneath the bank where prying eyes were not likely to come.

It was early in the melt when Jean and Anton went on their lone hunt. Around the colony the lal bushes were still in bloom. Now the siskal and greenhorn had both bloomed in turn and all three were fully leaved, only a few purple blossoms still clinging to the greenhorns. The gluegrass was a solid carpet as far as one could see.

Jean paused outside the Chambard's door until Chloe's mother appeared. No, she replied, Chloe was not at home but would probably be back soon. Jean was surprised and a little hurt, but not so much that he missed the strange look the older woman gave him. It made him thoughtful as he walked down to the wharf.

The barges were loading for the hunting kraals up-river. Scouts had brought word that the main herd had arrived along the Lydia. Two-thirds of the able-bodied men in the colony would be out hunting, nearly three times as many men as there were firearms. Of course the rest of them would not be unarmed, but a bow is a poor weapon with which to face an adult trihorn or a prowling longneck.

Jean had nearly reached the wharf when he heard Chloe's footsteps. She was coming from the north end of town, not from her parents' house. That puzzled him; later he would see greater significance to the fact.

He stepped into an alleyway with her so that their good-byes could be private.

They were thirty to a barge, but none rode. Twenty strained at the traces like dray beasts, dragging the obdurate devices against the current, while ten stood guard—four with the offworld double rifles, six with Levi-Stuer's muzzleloaders. Once they were beyond the town, they would be fair game for leers, trihorns, humpox, and longnecks. There were six barges, their crews assembled by lot. Jean had been chosen to man the third outpost, seventy kilometers upstream; he pitied the unlucky ones who had been chosen for outpost number six.

They made twenty kilometers a day and at night anchored in midstream. After the first day they saw animals everywhere, vast herds that came *en masse* to water at the river. The herds seemed as endless as the stars, but in three weeks they would be gone, chasing the melting snows southward, leaving the bushes and gluegrass churned and mutilated behind them.

Outpost three was simply an earth and stone enclosure four meters high and twenty meters across with no openings to the outside. The crew entered by climbing the rough walls.

Lone hunting was almost a sport, and had aspects of glory. Not so the communal hunts. They were all business; they put meat in the locker. As soon as the barge was moored and their meager supplies were inside the circle, it began. One man, rifle-armed, would set out with two others to make his kill. Then he would stand guard while his companions butchered. Load the meat in the hide, drag it back to the enclosure, and trade off, one of the butchers taking the rifle, the former rifleman taking up his knives. And so on, from earliest morning until dusk gave the advantage to the longnecks.

At night they ate cooked meat. When hunger overtook them on the hunt, they ate as they butchered, raw. It was brutal, mankilling work and it was dangerous; for each trihorn or herby the hunters killed,

73

they had to kill at least one krat or longneck intent on robbing them. The nights were punctuated by gunfire and the men praised the three moons for the light they gave. The plains became littered with bones and entrails as the colonists gathered a year's meat in three weeks.

Anton Dumezil was among the men assigned to outpost three. Jean saw him in the course of his work, but exchanged no word. Anton's earlier irritability had hardened into a sullen hatred. Why, Jean did not know. Three times the two were assigned to hunt together and did so without comment, but the strain was noticeable.

The supply of meat grew until longnecks and krats were constantly scaling the walls in vain attempts at theft. Claude Delacroix assigned more men each day to the task of guarding the enclosure. By the third week, eight men were standing guard while the rest worked, one hunter tó one butcher. The work of butchering a trihorn alone had to be experienced to be believed. Still the hunter had to stand guard, so the butchers simply gritted their teeth and continued, knowing that the hunter who stood guard would be down there butchering the next beast when turnabout came.

On the seventeenth day, Jean and Anton were assigned to hunt together. Anton accepted the rifle, a muzzleloader, and they went over the wall with first light.

The ground was littered with freshly picked bones where the krats had cleaned up after the hunters. The herds had thinned considerably and the bushes were torn and tattered. The pair went straight downriver for nearly a kilometer without spotting game. Finally Anton decided to drop down and try along the river.

Jean had his bow out, arrow nocked, when they came upon a trihorn—an old bull without a mate. There is no meaner animal than a trihorn in full rut and unable to find a female. He heard them, turned and charged.

Anton threw up his rifle but didn't fire—wisely, for

only the one load stood between them and death. He sidestepped right as Jean sidestepped left and then Jean released his arrow.

It was a deliberate act, an act of faith such as men who hunt dangerous game together must make. The arrow could not stop the trihorn; it could only divert its charge toward Jean.

The trihorn charged past Anton, presenting a perfect broadside target. A perfect setup. Anton swung the rifle.

He did not fire.

Jean was poised; he was so certain of the flash and the report that his mind heard what his ears did not. The trihorn did not falter; it did not fall to its knees, heart shot. Jean was momentarily paralyzed by his expectations and when he hurled himself aside, it was too late.

The upper point caught him in the left thigh and pierced to the bone. He felt the shock; heard the grating of horn on bone; felt himself lifted. Jean looked down on the earth as a bird looks, from above, saw the back of the trihorn, saw Anton's white face, saw the ground rush up.

There was talk of amputation and Jean screamed. Then he felt pain such as he had never known and he lost consciousness knowing that his leg was gone.

Somewhere in Jean's crazed world of pain, he found the will to move his hands. He found a great mound of bandages but there was still a leg beneath it and he let a calmer unconsciousness take him.

The delirium lasted for weeks, first from pain, then from infection. Certain bacteria are highly resistant to antibiotics, and one such lives in the trihorn dung which coats the ground in the time of the melt. All this Jean knew from later report; he remembered nothing except pain and fear.

Jean woke. It was a sudden thing; after weeks of madness, the fever broke in the night and he woke with his full faculties, but weak, incredibly weak. He was in his own bed in his parents' house. The quilt which lay over him was the one his mother had sewn of krathide the year she died. Jean had slept under it for nearly a decade.

Outside the ground was bare and brown. The shutters were closed tight but he could see through a crack. Another crack near the ceiling let a ray of light fall across his hands. They were fearfully thin. The ground outside told him that the melt had passed and the single shutter told that full winter had not yet come. Later, double shutters would be hung with dry leaves as insulation between them. At least a month had passed, but not more than two.

Jean remembered everything up to the moment he was hurled to the ground. He wanted to see his leg, but it took a long time to get the energy to throw back the quilt. When he did, he found his leg was wrapped in bandages and he got a look at his body. White; skeleton thin. The bandages were not bloody, and Jean was determined to see what lay beneath them. He nearly passed out from the effort of removing them; then he wished that he had.

The scars were massive, ridged, and ugly. That he could live with. But the bone had been broken and Jean could see that it had not set properly.

He moaned when he passed out, and his sister found him uncovered and unbandaged when she came rushing in.

A week later broth and renewed appetite had restored some of his strength. He found that much had happened during his unconsciousness. He had lain at the edge of death from infection and that was why, despite Doctor Marcuse's undeniable skill, his leg had healed crookedly. It was a wonder that it had healed at all.

And Anton had married Chloe.

Looking back and pondering—there was certainly time enough for that now—it all made sense. Chloe had never been what Jean would have termed faithful. That she had been seeing Anton at the same time she was seeing him was no great surprise—in retrospect. It also explained Anton's late-blooming hatred.

Why had he not fired?

Jean had to have the story, but he had to get it carefully. If it were an obvious lie, he had to consider whether or not to refute it. What could Jean accuse him of—attempted murder? Or failure under pressure, which carried as stiff a penalty and greater shame. Would such an accusation be fair?

Furthermore, Jean had to consider whether or not he wanted to make an enemy who might call him out to fight. Once that would not have bothered him, but now . . .

Anton's story, as Jean got it from Claude Delacroix, was that he *had* fired as the trihorn passed—that is, he had pulled the trigger but the primer failed. He then recocked the rifle and took new aim, but held his fire rather than hit his partner. When the trihorn tossed Jean away, Anton killed it.

The story could have been the truth. Or it could have been a lie, and no one but Anton would ever know. Primers do fail, though rarely.

Jean could make no accusation.

Chapter 10

The elders find low winter a gloomy time, though Jean could not imagine why. The sky is clear most days and when it is not, the high ice crystals which pass for clouds make beautiful patterns. Of course, there is no vegetation but there is never vegetation except during the melt or where there is liquid water—along the river, surrounding the lake, and, of course, in the irrigated fields. When high winter arrives and the snow comes, the elders seem better contented, saying that the snow covers the barrenness of soil and rock. Jean simply could not imagine what it might be like to live where vegetation was a year-round thing. He loved the melt as well as the next person, but he also treasured a return to the lean cleanness and the simplicity of rock and soil.

The streets were compacted earth again, now that the muds had gone. Jean leaned on his cane and started out again after resting against the side of a building. He was still very weak and his leg never stopped hurting. For a week he had been exercising near his father's house and this was the first journey of any length he had tried. Across the settlement to the house that Anton and Chloe were occupying.

He knocked on the door and waited, his breath freezing in a circle against the rough wood. That was the curse of low winter; every breath sucked a man dry and he must drink water by the gallon. Chloe opened the door and stepped back in horror.

"Good day, Chloe," he said.

From within the house all sounds ceased as Anton, unseen, froze at whatever he was doing. After a moment Jean heard his footsteps approaching and greeted him as he entered the room.

Anton's reply was half-hearted at best. Jean tried to interpret the look in his eyes. Hatred? Fear? Mere uneasiness? It was more than Jean could manage.

"It is good to see you up and around," Anton said. Jean ignored him and turned to Chloe. "You didn't come to see me during my convalescence."

She opened her mouth; closed it. Then she turned angrily and went to sit by the fire. Anton replied for her, "She has been busy. It's not easy to start a household."

"I wouldn't know."

Now Anton was really angry, but holding it back. Jean had him at a disadvantage for he made no accusations. He did not ask Anton what had happened —why he had not fired. Anton wanted Jean to ask so that he could defend himself against the unspoken accusation; or, better still, to deny Anton's story so that Anton could attack. Jean said nothing except, "You have something of mine."

Chloe stiffened.

"I have nothing that is yours," Anton replied.

"Yes, you have something that is mine by right of pain and I have come to take it."

Chloe stared her amazement. Jean was crippled, but he carried his blade. He smiled and said *sotto voce,* "Not you, *ma petite.* You I can live without." Anger took her color and he wondered what he had ever seen in her. Walking past her, he took down a trihorn antler from the mantle.

"What are you doing," Anton shouted. "That's mine."

"A trophy? These are as common as rocks. What makes this one so special?"

Anton said nothing.

Jean measured the antler against his cane, then tossed the cane into the fire.

"This is the horn that tore out my leg. You've said so many times, so it is reported to me. Very well, let the beast who crippled me provide my cane. I say that *I* own this antler, *n'est-ce pas?*"

Slowly Anton nodded, looking as if Jean had cut the thing from his body.

Jean turned at the door. "It is fitting that I should have this. A payment of debts. I always pay my debts.

"And others always pay their debts to me."

Perhaps it was the foolishness of youth that impelled Jean to do it, but he didn't think so. Youth has no monopoly on foolishness. Jean never mentioned the incident to anyone, nor ever again mentioned his "accident." Within the small community there was no one who didn't know the story. He carved a bone handle at the base of the antler and never walked with any other cane.

He could have lived on his past work and on sympathy, but that was not his way. He could not say that he did not despair or that he was not bitter. He railed at his weakness, at the fates, and at the untrustworthiness of his friends. Yet he kept his feelings to himself.

Jean would never walk straight again; therefore he could not hunt, for he was in no condition to hunt alone and no one would trust his life to a crippled hunting partner. Not even his fathers or brothers would have been so foolish. So be it.

The colony was only twenty years removed from an advanced, mechanized civilization, and the colonists were farmers. Yet few native plants would grow on their irrigated farms, and the vast herds were their true livelihood. To be a hunter was to be a man.

To be unable to hunt was to be emasculated.

Putting it so crudely was unfair to a subtle state of affairs, but it was true.

This, too, Jean had to accept, or at least to find a way around. It was for that reason that he took back the antler. A highly symbolic act.

That Anton had allowed Jean to take it without challenging or killing him on the spot was an admission of guilt. Jean could have ruined him with the story, but did not. Yet he walked with the antler cane and speculation followed him. Several times someone asked if Anton had given him the antler, but Jean never answered and no one pressed him. The very question bordered on insult and no one risks a challenge unnecessarily.

Jean went to Levi-Stuer's smithy, limping along the street in the dry, cold winter sun. The old man admitted him and closed the door against the cold. Levi-Stuer had been born and raised on Bordeaux; judging by his age, Jean felt that he must have been about forty when the *Lydia* arrived. He had taught himself the art of gunsmithing from the computer's memory banks, aided, some say, by Jandrax. Jean had never known how much of the Jandrax legend to believe.

Jean leaned the antler against the wall, accepted the mug of chota, and told Levi-Stuer that he was ready to learn his trade.

Jean looked up from the lathe where he was turning a firing pin for one of the double rifles. Levi-Stuer was whistling a tune the young man had never heard before and, as Jean was a collector of tunes, he listened for a moment, memorizing. But it was only a fragment which Levi-Stuer kept repeating.

"Herbert," he called, "what tune is that?"

"Um? Was I whistling?"

"Yes, but I don't know the tune."

The gunsmith looked puzzled. "I don't know what I was whistling; I wasn't paying any attention."

Jean chuckled and whistled the fragment back to him. Herbert laughed. "I haven't heard that in years. My wife would disown me if she knew I knew it."

"That good, eh?"

"You bet! Listen." He sang it in a broken baritone, all about a *femme* of unlikely appetites and proportions. They laughed together until tears came.

Levi-Stuer leaned weakly against the bench and wiped his face. "If you tell anyone where you learned that one, I'll not forgive you."

"Never!"

Herbert had mellowed in the months since Jean first came to him. His life had been unutterably lonely before and Jean had wondered why he chose to make rifles rather than wield them, much as his community needed the weapons. Now he knew, though Levi-Stuer would never admit it. It was written in his red eyes and the way he leaned forward to inspect his work with an eye almost to the metal. Herbert Levi-Stuer, master gunsmith—before Jean's coming, the only gunsmith—was more than half blind. Jean didn't mention it, not wanting to shame the older man.

Jean limped over to the desk where they took their lunch, cradling his bastard child. It was a weapon such as that world had never seen, a normal muzzleloader with a long, tapering 10mm barrel and a normal hammer mechanism and trigger, but with a very short second barrel mounted where the forestock should have been. This second barrel was calibered to 17mm and fired from a separate hammer and trigger set forward of and below the first. No one else was the least interested in it because it weighed several kilos more than the already heavy muzzleloaders; but then, no one else had had such a pointed reminder that single-shot weapons are not satisfactory for dangerous game.

Jean accepted a mug of chota and set to sanding the stock. He worked on his personal project only when no other task was pressing. Herbert watched for a moment, then chuckled, "Andrax would have liked that weapon. It would have appealed to his way of thinking."

Jean was curious. "Andrax? You mean Jandrax?"

"Jan Andrax was his name. It was only after he left that people bastardized his name."

Jean laid his pet aside. "People say that he designed the muzzleloader."

"That he did, and a fine job, too. In all my studies since I have never seen a simpler design that would be workable with our limited technology. Take that thing of yours. No offense, but the effort you put into it could have produced two normal muzzleloaders."

"I know. I would like to design a true double rifle like the offworld guns, but every time I try to get one off paper it turns out too heavy."

"Exactly! Andrax was a genius. We would never have made it without him."

"You said 'in your studies *since*.' Do you mean that Jandrax—Andrax—designed the muzzleloader before you became a gunsmith?"

"Oh, yes, he taught me the trade. I used the computer but he made the subject come real in my mind. Quite a man."

"What happened to him?"

The older man froze. Jean had seen the elders do that so often and always in response to the same question. What was there in this person that was so special? Some special honor or some special horror?

Chloe was pregnant. Jean wondered if it was Anton's child or his own, or if it belonged to a third party. Probably not even Chloe knew for sure.

By the melt, Jean had learned his trade. The offworld rifles were wonders of simplicity, as were the Jandrax muzzleloaders. The latter had only a barrel and a stock, a flash hole which was stuffed with a paper primer, a hammer and a trigger and the two bolts on which they revolved, and one spring. Only two moving parts. The offworld rifles were complex only by comparison.

During the winter Jean had built fifteen muzzleloaders in addition to his personal weapon. The latter was a standing joke; "Dubois' Panic Pistol" the hunters called it. Jean didn't blame them, really. The true joke was that he had built himself a rifle at all since he was forever barred from hunting. He turned five of his weapons over to the council to be used on the hunt. That would buy him and his family meat for the winter, and well it should. Five rifles were worth more than five men, but the council drove a hard bargain. It was made up of hunters, naturally. The other weapons he gave to Herbert in exchange for his education. Levi-Stuer protested that the payment was too high, but Jean would have no man say that he was unable to carry his weight in the community.

If he seemed bitter, he was.

Paulette Dumezil had married. She was the last of Jean's agemates. The oldest unmarried girl in the community was now four years his junior and she was being courted by all the fine young men who would soon go out on their first hunt. They would blast their way to glory and manhood with the rifles he had built.

Bitter? He damned well was.

Within the courtyard of his father's house, Jean practiced walking without his cane, but he never went outside without it. It was not that he could not, but as long as he carried that horn, people would remember the man who was injured as well as what he had become.

This he also practiced. He had fashioned a metal hook and attached it a handsbreadth below the handle of his cane. With the cane in his left hand and his rifle in his right, he limped across the courtyard, then suddenly swung around on his good leg, going to a crouch, planting the cane like a tripod, and swinging the rifle up in one motion. The rifle barrels came to rest on the hook so that either barrel could be fired, his eye was at the sight, and his finger on the trigger. Not graceful, certainly, but quick enough. From the beginning of the maneuver until the hammer fell on an empty flashhole only four heartbeats elapsed.

He was no longer cheerful. His sister Marie had been more than patient with him but he knew that she could not wait to be married and rid of him. His father steered clear of him and his brothers avoided him.

He sat alone in the evenings staring into the fire— alone but for the constant pain—and wondered what he had done to deserve such a burden. Once he had not thought thus; once he had not complained or railed against his fate. But, then, once he had been whole.

Pierre did not remark when Jean ordered the hundred soft iron bullets, the primers, and the powder. After all, who would have more use for such than a gunsmith. He did seem to think it strange when Jean bought a small quantity of scrap copper, but shrugged it off with a layman's ignorance of the workings of a gun.

The copper was expensive, but necessary. Since the colonists had not found lead on Harmony, they cast their bullets from iron. These were all 10mm, for Andrax had designed the muzzleloaders to fire the same ammunition as the offworld rifles. Jean put twenty of these in a special mold and added molten copper to bring them up to 17mm. He filled a horn with powder, pocketed the deadly primers—carefully shielded against shock in trihorn-wool batting—and pocketed the bullets.

Raoul brought the gig around just as Jean had requested. Jean was sure that his youngest brother found him a little insane; probably the boy was right. Three laborious, painful trips were necessary to carry down the provisions he wanted. Then Jean climbed aboard alone, rowed out from shore in the twilight, and set the sail.

Chapter 11

Anton Dumezil, the elder, paused on the catwalk that surrounded the palisade. Leaning against the truncated tree boles, he stared out across the fields. The melt had come. The fields between the palisade and the lake were sheets of snowmelt, broken here and there by the coming green. The intricate webwork of canals which would prolong the greening far into low winter was hidden beneath the sheet of natural water. A few prams moved about, poled by anxious farmers, all old men and boys.

Eventually the question would come—was he fit to lead the colony now that he was no longer a hunter? He would hunt this year, as he always did, but it had been some years since he had carried his own weight. Rightfully, he should turn his rifle over to a younger, stronger man.

It was wrong that the young men should have such power, even though the meat harvest was of paramount importance. Levi-Stuer had been preaching that for years, only ceasing when that Dubois boy went to work for him last year. Anton had not listened and now he wished he had.

His father, old Marcel, would have listened. He was crazy, but he listened.

Now his eldest son conspired against him, though *he* would stand no chance in a political contest. Young Anton had hurt himself badly by allowing Dubois to be gored—the elder Anton had no doubt that it had been intentional—and had proved himself indecisive in letting Dubois live when a clean knife thrust into the already gaping wound would have opened the femoral artery, yet have gone unnoticed. Further, he had had the gall and stupidity to marry that Chambard girl while Dubois lay bedfast.

Still, young Anton might have pulled it off, for Dubois was discredited as a man by his crippling injury. But then the boy had let Dubois take back that horn, a visible taunt and slur on his manhood. What a fool! What a coward! How could such a one have sprung from his loins?

Everything was crazy now. The young men wanted to take authority, forgetting that they, too, would grow old someday. It could not be that way, but how was he to stop it; though there had been few women —and too many of them had been lost to the *others*— those remaining had been fertile, and the younglings outnumbered their elders two to one.

Everything was crazy, but that young Dubois was the craziest of all, he and his bastard rifle. The council of hunters had demanded that Anton retrieve that weapon to be used in the hunt, ignoring the fact that young Dubois had contributed five rifles to the council and had made ten of those Levi-Stuer was renting. Fools! They should be honoring Dubois, not angering him. He had proved himself a man in the hunts, and further in his confrontation with Anton's eternally damned son. They counted him half a man because he was crippled, but such misjudgment always backfires. If they had treated him right, he would have made rifles for the next twenty years, becoming the single most important man in the community and vastly augmenting the colony's tenuous hold on civilization.

But they had not honored him; they had reviled him. Worse, their attitudes had so affected the impressionable young *femmes* that he was now without a mate. The asses! They should have banished young Anton and made Dubois a present of that slut Chloe.

Dumezil swung heavily away from the wall and worked his way down the ladder. Jean Dubois was his nephew, his sister Angi's son; why could worthless young Anton not have been more like him?

Lucien Dubois answered the door personally. Anton could hear Lucien's daughter working in the kitchen and could smell boiling meat. It was a sharp, rancid smell—year-old meat from the permafrost cellars. Soon there would be fresh meat to eat. Of all the things lost in coming here, Anton missed most the good French cooking of Bordeaux. Here there were not a dozen edible plants and a half-dozen edible species of animal. With such plain fare, eating had ceased to be a pleasure.

Lucien looked bad. Of course, Lucien always looked bad, thin to the point of emaciation, weak—tuberculosis probably. He should leave the household before his sons and daughter catch it, Anton thought, but where would he go? Still, Lucien seemed more distressed than usual.

"Lucien, old friend, you look troubled. What is it?"

Dubois motioned him to the wood and leather chair that sat by the fire, taking a stool before his honored guest. "It is my son, Jean. He has gone."

"Gone? Gone where? Where could he go?"

Lucien shrugged. "Who knows? He has been very bitter lately."

Anton nodded. "Perhaps he is keeping *liaison;* he has no wife. Maybe some great hunter is all talk and no manhood?"

Lucien looked puzzled, then took his meaning. "No, Anton, he is really gone. He took the gig, the one with sails, and left two nights ago."

Now this was news in a town where little ever happened. Anton was offended not to have heard. "Why was I not notified?"

"Why should you be? He committed no crime. If he wanted the gig, it was his. He was a *man.* He hunted so that we could have meat and he made rifles so that the colony would be stronger. Whatever I have is his if he wants it."

At mention of the rifle Dumezil was reminded of

his mission. "The bastard rifle, did he take it with him?"

"Of course, he was never without it."

This was bad. While the rifle was technically Jean's, the hunter's council wanted it and they would make things hard for Jean when he returned. If he returned. It occured to Dumezil that there could be only one destination for young Dubois. The gig could be sailed upriver even in the melt if the wind were as strong as it had been for the last two days. There he could hunt alone and perhaps recoup his status. It would be extremely dangerous; no, it would be suicide. He could never survive it.

Well, the damage was done. He would simply tell the hunter's council what he had found and they would look for his body. Or, rather, for the rifle.

On his way back from the Dubois house, Dumezil walked out to the hillock south of town where old Marcel was buried. Old man, he thought, staring down at the bare earth, why did you do this to us? You were the snake in your own Eden.

The sun was warm on Anton's neck, if only by comparison to high winter. He squinted as he looked around. Water everywhere, great sheets of it stretching from the lake to the base of the hills, the remnant of the winter's accumulation of snow. Soon all would be green again for a season. He remembered Bordeaux where the grass and trees were both kind and everlasting. Why, Marcel, *Papa, mentor?* Why this false *hegira?*

Positions on the barges were chosen by lot, but the elder Anton Dumezil had conspired to be assigned to outpost one each of the last five years. It made the trek easier for a man past his prime. The younglings were eager as always, poised for the slaughter. He could see little glory in sowing the ground with bones and entrails, though the hunt was a necessary pursuit.

Two-thirds of the male population went on the hunt, leaving behind only the women, the young boys, and a few older men like Levi-Stuer and Lucien Dubois. Chloe Dumezil cradled her infant son against her as she watched the barges depart carrying the younger Anton and the others. Her face was drawn with worry and disgust. It was clear that the men thought poorly of Anton, more for his surrender of the antler than for his actions during the last hunt. She had married him thinking him heir apparent to his father's power. It was clear now that he was no such person.

Night fell on a town that was nearly half empty. Levi-Stuer assigned guard posts to the boys and old men who remained. For many of the youngsters it was their first manly responsibility, and they strutted to their posts with bows strung and arrows bouncing at their hips. It was a pitiful guard, really, but Levi-Stuer was not worried. The *others* had not struck in several years and many believed that they had finally died out. They raided only during the hunt. Everyone seemed to accept that they simply struck when the guard was at its ebb, though some had suggested that they actually followed the herds. That was ridiculous of course; to do so they would have to travel thousands of kilometers a year.

Two nights passed without incident.

His name was Nightwind. He was slender but powerfully built, with no excess flesh. He wore herby hide breeches cut off just above the knee and high moccasins of longneck hide. He carried a bow and quiver which he hung in a greenhorn bush to protect them from moisture. His twin knives were of steel which he had forged himself, fashioning them lovingly over long hours. They were carried in a single sheath which was suspended horizontally before him, the blades overlapping, the handles projecting outward over each hipbone. He could draw either or both in a heartbeat. He wore no shirt, no jacket, and no cap.

The night was warm by the standards of Harmony, but none of the colonists would have dressed thus. Nor would Nightwind, had he been relaxing in his camp, but this was a mission where discomfort weighed second to mobility and he expected to remain active enough to make up for his lack of clothing.

The sun was down and Beta was up, shedding a silvery light. The fields were bloated with the excess snowmelt. He slipped from bush to bush, a shadow among shadows. Beneath the palisade wall he paused for a long time, listening. When his ears had confirmed what his eyes had seen from afar, he unwound the braided rawhide line from around his belly and made a loop, then flipped it effortlessly up to catch on the palisade wall.

He was over the wall in a moment, fading back into the shadows, coiling his line. Young Adrian Renou stood his guard, unaware that his perimeter of defense had been penetrated. Nightwind sneered.

He moved among the shadows all but ignoring the ineffectual guard and dropped to the ground. All of the doors in the town were bolted fast from the inside, so the Old Man said, but he knew where he could wait.

Slipping across the courtyard, Nightwind climbed to the second story of the town hall and the cubicle where Anton Dumezil made his home. He had personally watched Dumezil go out with the young men to hunt and knew that his wife was several years dead. It was a calculated risk that his apartment would be empty. It was.

Nightwind opened the shutters on the window overlooking the square and carefully carved out a notch. When he closed them again, they appeared unchanged, but he could watch the square unobserved. Satisfied, he dropped the bolt, wrapped himself in one of Dumezil's robes and slept.

Nightwind woke late in the morning and that shamed him. He had lived in the open all his life and the dim light of indoors had lulled him into thinking that the night continued outside.

He went to the window and stood watching the square. People came and went. Most were women since the men were hunting and the boys were sleeping late after a night on guard. Some of the women were attractive and these Nightwind watched with sharp attention. One in particular caught his eye.

Paulette Dumezil came to the cistern for water, carrying twin wooden buckets at the ends of a staff. She moved with an almost unconscious swaying of her hips though there was no one to see her. The cistern water was days old and sour; it rankled that she could not go down to the river for fresh water, but the hunter's council had declared that no woman should leave the palisade during the hunt. She could hardly remember the last abduction and discounted the danger. Taking the water, she returned to the cubicle where she lived alone now that her husband was on the hunt.

Nightwind tried to eat some of the supplies Dumezil had stored but found them unpalatable. He was used to fresh meat and fresh fruits. Ignoring the hunger in his belly, he lay down again in the afternoon to sleep. He had chosen his quarry and there would be no sleep tonight.

The moons moved in their complex patterns. Gamma was the first to rise, coming into view while the sun was still well up in the sky. Nightwind watched the sky for redness, though he could not see the sun from where he stood. Dusk came. Nightwind's skin shone red in the afterglow as he left Dumezil's apartment and slipped into the shadows. A few people were still on the street, but Nightwind had no difficulty avoiding them.

Nightwind stepped to the door and rapped sharply. In his left hand he carried a strip of supple hide and two hide cords. Paulette Dumezil opened the door, then opened her mouth to scream. He hit her.

Nightwind closed the door behind him and worked swiftly, binding her hand and foot and tying on the leather gag. He peered out again and saw no one. Heaving her to his shoulder, he padded down the street to the wall.

He could not climb the wall with his burden, nor lower her over the palisade with the guard nearby, so he left her at the foot of the ladder. When the guard had passed overhead, he went noiselessly up to meet him.

The guard stiffened and turned, bringing up his bow.

Nightwind smiled, crouched before him.

For a moment the guard was startled into immobility, and that hesitation was his last mortal act.

Nightwind wiped his knife, sheathed it, and dropped back to recover his quarry. Paulette was regaining consciousness so he struck her again, carried her up the ladder, and lowered her to the ground outside.

At midnight, Adrian Renou went to relieve the guard at the river wall and found him dead, his blade undrawn. In the furor and confusion that followed, it was several hours before anyone realized that Paulette Dumezil was no longer behind the palisade.

Chapter 12

Isle of Myth
Excerpts from the journal of Jean Dubois

The gig moves easily to the motion of the waves. I stare out across the endless waters, thinking back.

It has been fifteen months since the trihorn ripped my leg and made me a cripple. By now the herds will have come and gone, and all the men will once again have distinguished themselves. The young men will have taken wives.

Thinking back. And burning with hungers I can never appease.

Where do the herds go? Every year they come from the north, running with the melt. It has been thus since the *Lydia* arrived. Every year they come from the north, go south, but they never return from south to north. Therefore, where do the herds go, and where do the herds come from again the next year? People say the beasts cross the polar cap and return by following the northward melt on the other side of the planet. This is pure nonsense as anyone can tell from the reports in the computer. Jandrax—Andrax—may have known but he never passed the information on.

What happened to Jandrax? No one will tell and I could not find the answer in the landing craft's computer. Of course, I am no technician and the questions I can pose are quite elementary. I fear for our future. We have wrapped manhood up in hunting until no one who is not lame or blind will even smith the guns the hunters use. What madness. Only six of us still know how to run the computer.

Here is another mystery. The computer gave me the roll of the *Lydia*. Andrax was a supernumerary. There were eight crew members and one hundred colonists. None of the crew members still live. Why?

And what of the *precursors?* Who built the ruins that the elders sometimes mention? And who are those *others* whose existence the elders would like to deny?

The elders meet every such question with silence. They have fairly killed the curiosity of my whole generation.

I have with me a map of this region and another of the whole planet. I transcribed them painstakingly from the computer. It seems to me that the herds must follow the northward melt and that the only place they can do this is on the opposite side of the lake. That is a region as unknown to us as another planet. I am going there; again (and this question I must aim at myself), why?

Chloe's child should be nine months old now; simple arithmetic makes him a good bet to be mine, but Anton claims him. Perhaps; no one will ever really know. I saw him only once and I burned with a hunger that was nine-tenths shame.

There is nothing for me at the colony. The men despise me and the women shun me. So be it. They have cast me out symbolically, so I have cast myself out physically.

When I was younger I would have dreamed of finding where the herds go and returning triumphant with the knowledge. No more. Youth is dead, and dreams. Still I am curious, and out here on the open water my loneliness is less poignant than it was where I had my fellows around me, showing me by daily example that I am less than a man.

My supplies are limited but I have fishhooks and line. Every fish I catch sacrifices his entrails to make more bait so the supply is endless, if monotonous. I never dreamed how tired a man could get of raw fish.

I learned much from the computer before I undertook this trip, but little of it made sense. Now I have begun to put it together into a coherent pattern; the strange sounding names and terms are no longer meaningless. Keel, tack, tiller, before the wind. They were meaningless before. Now I know them well. Tacking is what I do from dawn to dusk, a keel is what I lack to do it well, leeway is what I am making—that is, the wind is blowing me away from where I want to go. Our lake is huge, 200 by 750 kilometers and I had intended to cross it diagonally. It seems that I will be at it forever and I would have long since died from my ignorance if I were on a terrestrial ocean, but there are no storms on this planet and I have only to reach out my hand to have fresh water. Water, fish, wind, sky, water. I live, but I become unutterably weary.

Using my knife, I make a notch in the calendar board as the sun sets, and count. Seventy-two.

By taking sun sightings at dawn and sunset I have been able to establish my latitude, but I have no way to determine my longitude. Each day finds me further south. It is now the seventy-fourth day of my journey and I have spotted land, but not the opposite shore of the lake. It is the great island which my map shows, or so I think.

I will stop here in hopes of finding the materials

94

with which to improve my craft, especially with which to build some form of keel. Also, I may find some of the smaller life forms here to supplement my diet of fish.

The island rose from the sea like the top of some mountain with great rocky headlands upon which the waves broke. On a planet without storms or rain, the rocky faces are stark and unweathered.

The island rose up devoid of vegetation, locked in the grip of low winter, the season of desert before the snows come. Only immediately adjacent to the lake was there a band of dense vegetation, drawing moisture from the lake itself. Here were giant trees whose roots must burrow down to water and whose boles thrust skyward, and beneath them layer upon layer of vegetation—saprophytes, mosses, lichens, an abundance of fruits and flowers, vines, and birds of all colors flittering between the layers of green. Yet even from my position at water level I could see the unyielding rock rising up behind the jungle, at places seeming only a hundred meters wide.

Nowhere on the planet have we found anything like this. Perhaps it is the moderating effect of the surrounding lake that allows such to develop. I do not know; such knowledge as I have is sketchy on these things. Perhaps Jandrax would have understood.

I sailed west around the island, looking for a safe anchorage. Were I whole, I could have run ashore anywhere, leaping out and dragging the boat up on some rocky shingle; with my injury I needed a place where I could tie up without beaching my craft. Once I entered the mouth of an inlet, dropping the unpredictable sail and rowing in, but the inlet was surrounded by low and swampy ground that I could not negotiate.

I stayed in that inlet, tied up to the knobby root of a low-growing tree and slept poorly, mindful of the new sounds around me. I did not hear the coughing of long-necks or the squeal of krats—for which I was thankful —but I did hear many sounds that I could not identify, especially a soft, crooning call that echoed throughout the night.

I missed the sunrise the next morning, shaded by trees and tired out by an uneasy night. When I woke, soft light was filtering through the jungle and the birds were about their daily tasks. I saw several species new to me and familiar species that were somehow different, like the leatherbill that landed on my prow, his brilliant red underbelly at odds with his continental cousins.

I caught rocod from the murky waters and ate them raw, but I kept my rifle close at hand, hoping that some herbivore would come down to water. I was thoroughly sick of raw fish. Leatherbills came to watch me eat, so I set my line again and, dividing my new catch, spent an hour feeding them. They were very bold, one even venturing to eat from my finger.

No herbivores came, nor had I really expected them. This fringe of jungle would be the abode of small creatures only. I saw what I took to be huge birds circling the island as I approached it yesterday, but they were not in evidence today.

I realized, with a twinge of guilt, that I had not notched my calendar board yesterday.

I spent the afternoon lounging in the boat. I had not realized the depth of my loneliness at sea; now it fell in on me again. In the afternoon I stripped and went overside for a much needed bath. At sea I had not dared do this for fear of becoming separated from the gig.

I considered sailing out to fill my waterskins rather than drink this muddy shoreline water, but I could not bring myself to leave this haven even for an hour. The next day I would go, however, for I was determined to find a landing where I could actually go ashore. I cursed my leg in bitterness, knowing that I had passed a hundred landings, including this one, where an agile man could have gone ashore.

When dusk came, the crooning resumed, alternating with an airy cry of, "Dilwildi, dilwildi, dilwildi." I searched the trees for the sources of the noise and saw patches of deeper darkness sitting at intervals along the larger limbs. Occasionally one of these would move, but I could not make them out. Alpha rose, with her tiny red companion Gamma in train. Beta, our third moon, would not be up for hours yet, but these two gave a silvery sheen to the lake, highlighting the darker gouges of the long, sweeping rollers. One of the patches of darkness detached itself from a limb and sailed seaward. I tracked it with my rifle, an instinctive, defensive action, but there was no reason to fire. It flew, but somehow I did not think of it as a bird. I followed it with my eyes until it was lost in the distance.

I slept too soundly that night. I had seen no carnivores, true, but there must be such or life here would quickly overpopulate. In the morning I slipped the oars into their sockets, cast off, and worked my way out of the inlet. I was in a foul mood, for rowing cost me much pain in my leg, yet I dared not set the unpredictable sail.

I rowed out into the lake a half kilometer to better survey the island, then turned west to follow the shore. The wind was against me, making the task harder than it need have been. From this distance I could see how thin the fringe of jungle actually was and how rugged were the hills beyond. Except for the shore, it was a forbidding and utterly inhospitable place.

I rowed for several hours, searching for a proper anchorage. I also filled my waterskins for the first time and set the line out to catch some fish more palatable than rocod. I had given up the idea of finding large game, but if I could get ashore and build a fire, cooked fish would be a delicacy by comparison.

At one point a flat plain no more than five meters above water level extended several kilometers inland. Here the jungle too thrust inland. There was an inlet into which I rowed.

It was not a river, of course, for there was nothing to feed it, yet it no doubt carried snowmelt from the mountains during the melt. Now the inlet was merely a thin arm of the lake, first a half-kilometer wide but soon narrowing to a dozen meters. My passage was silent but for the cutting of my oars, and the birds were in full song. Trees soared overhead, their branches intertwining to make tunnels of the smaller channels off the main stream. Twice I saw the large flying creatures overhead, but they passed quickly from sight.

I paused to check the charges in my rifle, for with a section of jungle this large I would have to revise my earlier assumption that there would be no large animals. It was my seventy-sixth day of raw fish.

The inlet continued for several kilometers, growing gradually narrower until trees began to meet over the main channel. I tied up to a tree and worked my way across the steps that its roots provided onto dry land. I staggered and nearly fell, so unaccustomed was I to the firm, unswaying earth.

The grass underfoot was not the ubiquitous glue-grass that the colonists hate. It did not cling to boots and clothing, carrying its mucilaginous spores. This grass was fine and sweet smelling, a pleasure to touch and an invitation to lie upon. I had heard of such grasses from the elders, but had thought them fantasy. The trees seemed even taller from beneath, and the profusion of birdlife and wildflowers was even more breathtaking than the soft grass and immense trees. Standing alone, cut off fully from my fellow man, I broke down into tears at the beauty around me and at the poverty of life as I had previously known it. Beside this, our settlement, our fields, and our silly pretensions to manhood looked pale and drab.

II

I stayed in that clearing for three days, living without shelter under the canopy of trees. On the first day I washed my clothes and built a bonfire to dry them. Then I bathed again and luxuriated in a clean body, cleanly clothed. I cooked the fish I had caught, but I did not see any large herbivores, nor did I wish to try to kill any of the small creatures around me. Never had I seen such a profusion of life except in the migratory herds during the melt, and I did not wish to subtract as much as one creature from it.

Each night I heard the crooning and the incessant "dilwildi, dilwildi." I saw the large flying creatures several times at a distance during the day and every night close up in the darkness. I was convinced that they were not birds.

There is a creature called a milik which feeds on the dried seedpods of the siskal. There are never very many of these creatures and they are quite small, but they do provide a certain amount of sport and a bit of fresh meat in the off seasons. In order to snare them, boys often row far upstream on the Lydia during low winter. Six years ago, my father got the idea of attaching a sail to our gig and sailing upstream before the wind, then drifting back down. Since then several others have copied his idea.

Papa never had to contend with tacking against the wind, so his gig had neither keel nor centerboard. The sail itself was a large, clumsy square of sewn up herby hides. After ten weeks at sea I was only too familiar with the gig's shortcomings.

Refashioning my rigging into a lateen pattern and building sideboards took the better part of three days, after which I decided to hunt. Though I had not wanted to set snares for the smaller creatures, I was not reluctant to face a herby and there were herby tracks in abundance along the inlet.

Herbys are burro-bodied, tapir-headed, earless, and tailless herbivores. They are devoid of defense, depending on their speed, agility, and prodigious birthrate to perpetuate their species. I had seen no large herbivore tracks other than these and no large carnivore tracks at all. This was an oddity, for without carnivores to thin their numbers, the herbies would soon have eaten the island into barrenness.

Several times I had heard the herbys come to drink during the night, so after finishing my work in the gig I slept away the afternoon in preparation for a night hunt.

Of course I could not stalk, but I had discovered their favorite watering place and took my place in the lower branches of a tree waiting in ambush. They came after midnight and I had calculated right in getting myself downwind of them. I killed one cleanly as he stooped to drink.

The herd scattered with cries of terror and the forest night sounds fell silent. For a moment I felt exultation, then a nameless dread. It was as if I had sinned in the face of God. Never had I felt such guilt.

Some *presence* moved in the jungle night.

Something sleeping was wakened; something quiescent was angered.

Some *thing* became aware of my presence. I could feel its personality as it probed and quested.

I did not move.

The spirit of the place moved in the moonlit glade. A breeze stirred the trees, flattened the grass. The herby lay on its side, feet stretched stiffly toward me, lying in an obscene black pool of its own blood.

I dared not move, yet the *thing* found me. It moved in the tree beside me where no material thing could be seen.

Spiraling above the clearing, rising from somewhere inland, I saw the heavy flying things that had eluded me during the day. They rose like a cloud, circling, like some great aerial hieroglyph. Their cries came down to me, "Dilwildi, dilwildi, dilwildi."

The *presence* sat unseen beside me in the tree, its essence scratching at the surface of my mind, seeking entry, finding none.

"No!" I was whimpering like a child in the treetop, overcome by some unspoken guilt. I was a man, a hunter. What business did I have with such feelings. Yet they were not to be denied.

The flying things decended to the clearing, making a circle around the dead herby. One slipped forward, scuttling crabwise to investigate this incursion of violence into a realm that knew no violence. How did I know that? Yet I did.

They were clearly creatures of the air who moved

clumsily on land. Their wings were disproportionately long and seemed not feathered but furred; beyond that I could tell little about them.

Over the course of millennia, legions of demons have crept into earthly folklore and scores of these have made their way into the Monomythos. In my imagination, they sat with me that night.

The flying creatures left the ground in a concerted rush, flying laboriously into the trees. They had come from the rocky fastness at the center of the island.

Within me was a desire to follow them, to track them to the place of their origin. Was this my own wish, or something left me by the *presence?*

Then I realized that it was gone and I was alone again.

When morning came, I had not slept, nor had I left my perch. At first light I reloaded the upper barrel of my rifle. I had not dared to do so in the dark for fear of overcharging it. I dropped down from the tree, recovered my cane, and limped out to the herby. The meat would be rank for not having been bled, but my hunger could overcome any delicacies of appetite.

I laid my rifle close at hand and drew my knife. I would cut a steak and broil it.

I could not.

I stood with my knife poised and could not bring it down to lay back the skin and expose the firm, red meat beneath.

Cursing myself for a child, I plunged the blade in angrily. The firm flesh gave before my blade and I shuddered at its texture, though it was a texture I had known all my life. What was wrong with me?

I laid back a flap of skin from the haunch, forgetting to skin the beast properly. There was a stricken gasp from the trees where the unseen audience of flying things waited. Yet it had not been an audible gasp; I had heard it in my mind. I cut out a steak, though my hand trembled so that I could hardly control it. The mass of flesh which came out was misshapen and bloody. My stomach contracted.

It had returned and *it* was appalled.

Cursing, I carried my steak to the edge of the trees and built a fire. I impaled and broiled it. The juices dripped from the meat and sizzled in the fire while my stomach turned flips in anticipation. Let phantoms be damned; I was hungry and I would eat. I took the steak down half raw and sank my teeth into it.

I gagged. The blood juices were a fire in my throat and I barely avoided vomitting. How could I ever have eaten meat before? I threw the steak aside.

One of the flying creatures left its sanctuary and floated down to me. It was mammalian; its wings were covered with a tight, furry skin. I was reminded of stories of terrestrial bats, but this creature inspired no loathing. Its weight was about ten kilos and its wingspread greater than the reach of my arms. Its belly was round; like the herby it was earless and tailless. Its face was whiskered, looking for all the world like a terrestrial seal, and its expression was both benign and bemused.

"Dilwildi!" it said, so I named both the individual and his race after that sound. The creature looked up at me as if deciphering some great puzzle, then sat back with a thump, scratching its plump belly. "Dilwildi," it announced again and I broke into laughter. It was not offended; rather, the tiny face seemed to beam even more happily.

The dilwildi drew up his wings and flapped heavily across the glade to a siskal bush, here of treelike stature. He slipped clumsily from branch to branch, then returned bearing a half-dozen siskal fruit which he gave to me. I bit into one and never had fruit tasted so good.

III

The dilwildi stayed with me throughout the day and his brethren from the trees dropped down by ones and twos to inspect me. I laughed insanely at their antics and wondered if my mind was slipping from being too long alone. They were friendly and inquisitive creatures who got into every part of the gig and all of my belongings, save one. They would not approach the rifle. This I could not understand since they had not seen it used, nor could I understand my revulsion from meat. Finally I dismissed the dilwildi's actions as a dislike of the smell of gunpowder and my revulsion as a stomach too long accustomed to raw fish.

For all my rationalizations, I could not dismiss the *presence* I had felt.

I slept most of the morning, making up for the night, and when I woke the dilwildi were still with me. I felt a nameless restlessness and a desire to explore.

Leaving the gig, I limped inland, avoiding the glade where the dead herby lay. For hours I walked, eating from time to time of the fruits available. Siskal and lal were both in fruit, though they never fruited at the same time near the colony. Here, I thought, would be the ideal place to move our settlement, but no sooner had the thought occurred than I was dumbstruck with grief as I pictured the destruction of the paradise by my brother hunters.

I had gone about two kilometers when my way was blocked by a rock ledge overgrown with brush. I did not know how far it extended in either direction, so I tried to climb over. My antler cane slipped on the first rise and tore away the turf.

I viewed the exposed material with amazement. Neither rock nor soil, but flaky rusted metal. At first I thought this was the remains of something lost during the colonization, but our artifacts would not have gone to rust so quickly. Whatever lay here predated man's arrival on Harmony. I surveyed its length and breadth in wonderment. It could be the weckage of some air or space craft, but I thought not. Once, we are told, this planet's ice caps must have been smaller and at such a time the sea level would have been higher. This, I felt, was the remains of some gigantic sea vessel, lying where it had come to rest on what had been the bottom of the sea.

I circled the wreck, if such it was, and continued inland. The dilwildi accompanied me, flying in intricate patterns above me. Always one or more of them flew just above me or waddled beside me. Occasionally one of them brought me fruit. My guides, for so I thought of the ones who stayed near me, eased my path by pointing out game trails and twice led me to seeps of clear, cold water.

Still it was not an easy journey for me and my leg ached abominably by midafternoon. I sat in a sunny glade and brought together the makings of a fire, determined to go no farther that day. I piled a pyramid of kindling and took out my flint and steel, but the afternoon was warm and somehow I lost interest in making a fire. I put the flint and steel back in their packet.

Suddenly, I was scared. First the meat, then the call to the interior, and now this. My will no longer seemed my own.

How had I concluded so readily that the overgrown ridge was a ship? It seemed more sure than a surmise. Somehow, I *knew*.

I took out my flint and steel. I wanted no fire; I abhorred the very idea of fire. How could a man desire a fire in this sunny glade?

I struck flint to steel.

The *presence* was there, sitting unseen beside me in the grass, somewhat irritated but also greatly intrigued. I could feel its curiosity at my acts. Involuntarily, I turned my head but found nothing.

I lay back in the sun and slept.

I woke shortly to find that my kindling had burned down to ash. Why had I slept? Was it exhaustion or had I been ordered to sleep so that the fire would die?

Suddenly I wanted no more of this island. I took up my cane and turned back toward the shore.

The dilwildi were arrayed in a crescent, barring my path. There was neither anger nor hostility in their expressions. Rather, their entire attitude was of sorrow and hurt. Still they frightened me, lined up against me as they were, and I reached for my rifle.

I could not find it.

For the first time since I had built it, I had forgotten it. It lay with my belongings near the gig.

I turned downslope toward the dilwildi. They closed about me, mewing with the soft cry I had heard in the night, a heart-rending cry of sadness entirely unlike their exuberant "dilwildi." They closed about, gripping my legs, restraining me gently. In fear as much as in anger, I struck out with my cane. One of the dilwildi was bowled over, bleeding from parallel cuts where the antler tip had caught him.

Instantly they retreated, ringing me with a wall of shocked horror. The *presence* was likewise horrified.

I fell to my knees, tears streaming, my insides torn and twisted at the thought that I had harmed so harmless a creature. I fell forward and buried my head against the earth. There was cold on my shoulders and I looked up to find the sun obscured by clouds—clouds on a planet that knows no clouds. Fear was in me, but more so a load of guilt so great that I could not bear it. I buried my face again.

They surrounded me then, burying me in a mass of soft, furry bodies, each tiny creature radiating good will and forgiveness. I slept.

When I woke the sun was up on a new day. I had slept warm under a blanket of living fur and only now did the dilwildi stir themselves and rise. One lay near my face and as I rose he looked inquiringly at me. I could see the twin weals across his belly. Raising his tiny hand, he touched my face and traced down to my chin. I drew myself awkwardly into a sitting position and faced him, ready for whatever message he bore, but if he was a messenger, he was mute. He waddled up and slipped into my lap like some huge cat, stretching and watching me with an intensity that provoked my laughter.

All that morning we worked our way higher and inland until at noon we had reached the barrier presented by great balks of stone set into what I knew to be a pier. How I knew, I could not have said, but it came to me that they sat at the edge of a fossil ocean and that the jungle I had traversed was the floor of some long-dead bay.

The dilwildi led me by way of an ancient path to the foot of the piers. Here we were above the jungle in the tangle of waterless rock that formed the central majority of the island. It took me most of the afternoon to painfully make my way to the top of the pier. I had concluded that after spending the night there I would have to return to the jungle, for here there would be neither food nor water.

I stood on the mighty pier and looked inland at what had once been an island on a salty sea and saw in my mind's eye trees, parks, and boulevards where now lay only waterless waste and ruins.

For there were ruins. Before me lay an entire city, stripped by the elements until only the stones remained. From the sea I could have looked at this mountainside and never guessed that the barren rocks I saw were the sole remnants of the handiwork of man.

Man—or something else.

I wandered the streets of the ruined city with my cadre of furred companions. The wind whistled in utter loneliness theough the ruins that once had sheltered—what? Man? Some humanoid creature?

Or were the dilwildi the descendants of those who had built this city, generations removed from civilization and reverted to precultural savagery?

Then I knew. The dilwildi were the pets of those who had built the city. For generations they had been bred for docility, for gentleness, and for the savoring of human (?) company. That they survived their masters in loneliness was perhaps the greatest tragedy wrought here.

How I knew this, I could not have said, but I had experienced too much to question such knowledge.

One building was somewhat better preserved than the others. The dilwildi led me to it but would not accompany me in. It was hardly ten meters across and circular, a ring of smooth metallic columns which had once supported the roof that now lay in ruin. I picked my way among the rubble toward the center of the circle and sat down, watching the sun set to the west. A great lethargy took me and I closed my eyes.

IV

She woke me to a golden dawn. The floor where I lay was carpeted with rugs woven in alien and intricate patterns but otherwise the building was bare of furnishings and open to the gentle breezes that rose from the sea bearing the scent of salt and fish.

She was a study in perfection, a dream made flesh. Varicolored eyes, tumbled hair of a hue not auburn but *red,* deep, brazen, absolute red, skin of copper fading to cream beneath her breasts and beneath her arms where the sun could less readily go. She wore a chain girdle of silver supporting a golden *ankh;* otherwise she was naked.

Rising from her shoulder blades were wings like those of some gigantic butterfly. Not the feathery white wings of an angel, nor yet the leathery red wings of a demon. Spreading, rounded, varicolored wings.

She beckoned me to rise and I did so, following her outside. The city spread out before me, an aching mass of color. The piers I had so laboriously climbed were now at the water's edge. Tied up to them were ships of all sizes and descriptions, others lying at anchor in the bay beyond, under which lay, or would lie, the jungle I had trod.

She turned to me and extended her hand, fingertips touching my forehead. "Welcome," was the sound that echoed in my head with suggestions of a lark-bright voice. "We are pleased that you come." Then she withdrew her fingers and spoke, watching my face intently as she did. I heard in my ears the lark voice that had been in my mind, but her words were a meaningless trilling—pleasant but unenlightening. She cocked her head.

107

Another of her race joined us, floating in on wings of fiery color. He landed lightly beside her, his wings making soft thunder in the morning air. He, too, was beautiful; like her he wore only a loinstrap of chain, but supporting a *lingam*. His body was hairless and the hair on his head was white and tangled, but gave no impression of age. His eyes were varicolored, changing as he turned to speak to her. His voice too was larklike and incomprehensible, but there was no trace of femininity about him. Fine muscles moved beneath his skin as he shifted his weight. They conversed in their own language for several minutes without attempting to translate for me, then he left, flexing his legs to bound into the air, spreading his mothwings and catching the rising sun on the iridescent fur that covered them; he was gone with a muted rush.

Across the city I could see many like him fluttering here and there, making the morning bright with the colors of their wings. No two were alike and each was an intricate working of several colors, not all of which would have been considered appropriate by a terrestrial artist; yet here they were. I realized that I was looking at the original pattern from which the rugs on which I had lain were taken.

Not all the flying shapes were humanoid. The air was filled with the soft cries of tiny furry things singing out their unending paean: "dilwildi, dilwildi."

Was she the *presence?* The instant I asked myself the question, I knew that she was not.

She motioned for me to follow her and, taking pity on my wingless condition, led the way walking. Apparently this was the same city I had seen in ruin, nor was my memory in any way damaged. This was either an intricate dream (which I did not believe) or I had somehow been transported spiritually or bodily to the time when it had been in full flower. And flowering it was, with such a profusion of plant life as to make my jungle seem a desert by comparison. It was like a giant park, with every tree and shrub and ground hugging turf designed to please human or quasi-human senses.

My winged companion led me to a park where we sat beneath a tree that seemed to have ancestored the lal, although its fruit was larger and seemed more succulent. We sat in silence, she enjoying the beauty around us, while I tried to make sense of it all. Across the turf from us a group of children was tumbling playfully upon a long suffering herby, clearly one not only domesticated but a pet. The children's backs were deformed (to my alien eye) by crumpled growths, clearly wing buds. The herby looked at me as if for delivery from his small torments and a flock of dilwildi settled down in the park, capturing the attention of the alien children.

My companion apparently felt that I had had enough time to adjust to my surroundings, for she wiped the fruit juices on her bare thighs and reached out to touch my forehead.

"I am Aeolios."

The sound was in my head and I answered aloud in my own language, "I am Jean Dubois."

"Welcome to our land, Jeandubois."

"Where—or when—am I?"

She paused, considering. "You are on an island, the same island to which you sail. Your second query has no meaning to me."

Ignoring her odd, tenseless grammar, I tried again. "When I arrived on the island, your city was not here. I went to sleep in a ruined building and when I woke the building was not a ruin, nor was the city. I surmise that I have been transported to some past time."

She broke contact and screwed her face in thought. Clearly baffled, she raised her hands to her own head and seemed to be in communication with some other person or thing. For long minutes she remained thus, then she opened her eyes and extended her hands to me again. "You refer to the theory of chronology, wherein time is seen as a linear process. That theory has no validity. Could you rephrase your question?"

"Of course it has validity. What was here yesterday is gone today and what is here today is gone tomorrow. Men grow, mature, and die, leaving behind descendants. Nothing is more basic in the world."

She broke contact again, her face a mask of horror and pity. Immediately she raised her hands to her forehead and once more went into her trance.

She remained thus for so long that I gave up on her and wandered around the park. The children had gone but the herby remained. As an experiment I approached him and he turned to meet my hand, though clearly disappointed that I had not brought him some tidbit in exchange for his attentions. I touched him hesitantly, but he took no notice. I stroked his neck in amazement. We have no pets on Harmony, having nothing to feed them. I had never touched a living animal before, save the dilwildi who seemed more than animals. I was struck most by the herby's indifference to my attentions. He paid me no more mind than he had the playful children.

A winged male wandered into the park with a female and they settled beneath a tree, eating the fruit that hung down, then entangled in love making. I turned away, but my scruples were entirely my own. They were aware of me—they had made hand motions toward me that seemed greetings when they entered the park—but they were apparently without notions of modesty or privacy.

Aeolios emerged from her trance and crossed the park to me. There was a mixture of contrition and pity on her face as she touched my forehead. "I am sorry, Jeandubois. In my ignorance I think you mad, but in my understanding I know you are merely deluded. The masters tell me that you think the chronology to be real and that I should be patient with your lack of understanding. They say I am to tell you that, in your erroneous way of thinking, you are in the past, but that the term has no meaning. I am sorry, Jeandubois; it is all too much for me to understand, though I convey the message."

"Who are the masters?"

She struggled visibly with her confusion, but did not

break contact. "The masters are *the masters!* How can you ask such a question?"

"Have patience with my ignorance, Aeolios; I do not know your masters."

This time she broke contact and fled, stumbling away, then taking to the air. I watched her spiral up and disappear beyond the trees that circled the park.

V

I wandered about the city, trying to make sense of my situation. At first I had merely accepted things as they were or seemed to be, much as one will accept the reality of a dream world. Now I was no longer able to do so, and my fear grew. Where or when was I; how had I come here; why was I here; would I be allowed to leave? Lovely as the city was, it was not of my world.

Wherever I went the dilwildi followed me, seeming to spy on me. Were they servants of the masters, and were the masters the same personages as the *presence* I had felt before?

A winged male dropped beside me, scattering the dilwildi in clumsy haste. Unlike Aeolios, he had no smile for me. "The masters wish your presence," he announced.

"Excellent. I have a few questions to ask them."

Irritation crossed his face at my statement.

"One does not ask the masters questions. One hears them and obeys."

"Perhaps," was my only reply as I sought to restrain my own irritation.

He guided me through the maze that was his city, moving ever upward. I lagged behind, hampered by my leg, and he waited for me, his face as cold as the stones around us. My fear had been growing since I woke this morning and was now a knot in my middle. I was unarmed. My rifle and blade were at the gig and even my antler cane was nowhere in sight.

We walked down grassy paths through the heart of the city. There were no boulevards, for the winged people would have no need of them, only the paths where the herbys roamed free. Finally we reached a wall twice man-height that stretched away in both directions until it was lost in the trees. My companion trilled loudly and a trio of others like him dropped down to his aid. They gripped my shoulders and, beating their wings heavily, lifted me into the courtyard beyond.

It was a temple or palace, no doubt, but it was not greatly different from the city at large. Before me was a parklike expanse of trees and grass; in the center of the park was a pavilion like the one I had found myself in when I arrived here.

The winged men were gone in a rumble of wings before I could ask them what was to come next. Either they feared this place or the felt that even one such as I would know what to do here. In that they were mistaken.

The pavilion sat in the center of the park and was the most likely place to go. No doubt those who had ordered my coming expected me to enter it.

I picked a fruit from a nearby siskal, eased myself to the ground and turned my back to the pavilion. The fruit was exceptionally sweet and I was glad to get off my feet.

The *presence* returned. I ignored it and continued to eat.

Are you unaware of us?

"Of course not."

Then why do you ignore us?

"Among my people it is a gesture of contempt!"

The fruit was snatched from my hand, the sky darkened, the ground heaved, and I was thrown prone. Fear was in me, more fear than I had ever known. I strove to conquer it in the only way I could, by hurling curses at the *presence*. There was sudden silence.

There was more than silence.

There was a complete absence of light or sound, touch or feeling of warmth and cold. My mind was somewhere, still within my skull perhaps, but utterly bereft of sensory input.

112

I was alone, as utterly alone as human can ever be.

I was afraid, but that feeling passed.

I was beyond fear, but not beyond loneliness.

I was myself, but without others to lend boundaries to myself. I was everything; therefore I was nothing.

I was a lone dust mote floating forever in interstellar space and I was God. Nothing and everything; in the realm of uttermost loneliness both are the same.

As I was unbounded in space, so was I unbounded in time. My consciousness stretched eternally forward and backward and in that vast expanse there was none but me.

In the midst of nowhere, the *presence* came to sit by my side. It gestured with an absent hand and the stars shone about us. They wheeled in their courses and one grew until all others were occluded. About it swarmed planets and one of these grew until it blotted out the others. Gigantic polar caps receded and advanced and receded and advanced. Species were gained and lost until at last there rose a genus of winged animals capable of fleeing before the advancing ice. They multiplied and grew dominant. Species were formed and lost, but two outstripped the rest, one large and one small.

The *presence* made his will known on these unformed species and they worshipped him, but as their intelligence was imperfect their worship was imperfect, so the presence moved his will upon them and they were given speech. He made the larger dominant over the smaller and gave it intelligence far greater than the smaller so that even as the larger worshipped the *presence,* so the smaller would worship the larger.

Thus the world was made perfect.

Again the ice caps advanced and species were broken. The ice retreated and new species arose, horned and angry species, unlike the gentle creations of the *presence.* Only the dilwildi on this island and the herbys survived. The winged people were utterly detroyed.

Why?

The *presence* was not bound by the material world.

113

It did not perceive time as a unidirectional flow but as a stationary axis along which *its* perceptions could move at will. To the *presence* the winged people still lived at the height of their glory, as did the ice ages and the new law of antler and fang. All was not "good," for the concept had no meaning. All was. It was enough.

But now there was a disturbance in the all. The *presence* was questing for the source and meaning of the disturbance.

Intelligence was moving again on *his* planet. It had no place in his projection of the future, for this was a planet that could never produce intelligence, save when the *presence* moved in the world and made it so. This he had done once and was satisfied. That intelligence had come again was a negation of his powers of prediction.

It was a discontinuity in the all. *He* would investigate.

He observed the works of man, wingless man. *His* power was great, but here was a thing beyond *his* understanding so *he* bided *his* time. For one to whom eons were as heartbeats, the wait of a generation was not to be noticed. Then one came to the island! *He* moved to draw it to *him.*

And it had defied *him!* An insignificant creature that he could have snuffed with a thought; it had defied *him!*

None had ever defied *him* before. Anger warred with curiosity.

So it was that *he* took up the creature and showed it the wonders that were *himself.* Then *he* arrowed *his* consciousness into the pitiful mind before *him.*

Jean screamed!

The world was rocks and sunlight; harsh, unrelenting. No living thing moved. The wind sighed through the ruins and the dilwildi had gone.

Jean was alone.

He stood; swayed; pain was a living river of fire

114

surging through his body. The ruins lay before him, waterless and forgotten.

Dismissed. He had been tried and found insignificant.

Did Moses feel like this? *Should I carve tablets of stone to carry back from my Sinai?*

Jean's stomach contracted and his mouth was sand. Surely much time had passed since he had climbed the mountain. Starting down, he stumbled.

His crooked leg. *It* could have healed him, had *it* chosen to do so.

Should he take back his revelation to those who had cast him out? Should he claim holiness and its fruits— food for his table and a woman for his bed? A bitter taste of unlaughed jest was in his mouth. What woman could ever make him forget Aeolios?

Swaying slightly, the Prophet came down from his mountain.

Chapter 13

By Jean's calculations, the north tending melt would return to the latitude of the colony about 180 Harmony days after his departure. His excursion toward the center of the island had ocurred on the eightieth day of his journey so it was clear that he would need speed to reach the opposite side of the lake in time to catch the returning melt.

He need not have worried. The new sail and sideboards gave him speed and, more important, let him lie closer to the wind so that he could proceed more directly toward the west. Where before he had fought helplessly against the wind, he now cut purposefully toward the southwest on an endless tack. From first light until long after dark he held his course and every night he wrapped himself in the hide sail for warmth.

Every night he dreamed of Aeolios and her beauty, and he dreamed also of the *presence*.

Had it been real?

Thirty-seven days out from the island, Jean sighted the opposite shore of the lake in the sunset. By noon of the next day he had reached it and beached the gig. It was a low shore, icy and snow-covered. He had not brought skis, for his crippled leg prevented their use, so he was restricted to floundering near the shore. He shoveled away the snow from the lee of a cutbank and tore up the ragged remains of last melt's bushes to build a fire. Wrapped in the sail, he luxuriated again in the feel of solid earth.

He stayed overnight, basking in the warmth of the fire and planning. He roasted fish in the coals. In the morning he would start south, following the shore until he reached the melt.

He followed the shore southward for two weeks, beaching the gig each night for the comfort of a fire. Soon the snow showed signs of noon melting; the surface was glazed and hard when he went ashore in the late afternoon. Then it was still liquid in the afternoon. Two days later he began seeing patches of bare earth.

Now he was coming into dangerous territory. Soon the first of the leers and krats would appear if his theory was correct. He stopped sleeping ashore, but anchored just off shore and watched. The next evening he saw a krat. It cautiously descended to the lake shore searching for danger. Jean tracked it with his rifle, but his ammunition was too scarce to waste on such a small, bad-tasting carnivore.

The next night he saw tracks of leer and krats. In the morning he waited until nearly noon before abandoning his post. That night he saw leers but they were too wary to approach the gig.

Jean was becoming angry. His hunts had been frustrated before and he had taken it in stride, knowing that there would always be another day. But then he had been whole. Now he knew that it was his lameness that stood between him and a kill and he was getting almighty tired of fish.

He put out further into the lake and sailed south four days without approaching the shore, intending to reach the region of high melt. When he put to shore again the character of the land had changed completely. The snow was gone and the creeks were flowing bank-full in roiling, muddy flood. His visibility was restricted, but he could see the tops of the lal bushes waving in the wind and the lakeshore was a sea of muddy tracks.

It would be necessary to go inland to hunt but Jean doubted his ability to do so on foot, so he found a creek, furled the sail and bent over the oars. The flood washed about him as he struggled upstream. He had drawn the sideboards up to reduce both draft and drag. After half an hour of struggling he had not gained a hundred meters. The flood was simply too strong. He let the gig slip back downstream. He was too tired to curse.

Jean rode the current out into the lake, caught fish, and ate them raw. The pain in his leg became excruciating from the unaccustomed strain at the oars, but the pain inside his chest was worse. Once again he had been frustrated; once again the verdict of his peers had been vindicated—he was a cripple and therefore unworthy.

That night he relived in dreams a portion of his island ordeal, and when he woke he could not sort the memory of dream from the memory of reality. Had the whole affair been hallucination? A comforting thought, but Jean found himself clinging to the memory. He feared it, but feared more to lose it.

By faint moonlight he let semen fall into the water, then lay back, scarcely relieved, to mourn the passing of a fantasy.

He made a final pull on the oars and the gig grounded against the gravel beach. Shipping the oars, he lifted his bad leg overside, then pivoted on the gunwale and dropped into the shallow water. He took the painter and painfully dragged the gig higher up on the beach. Jean was going hunting. He might not return, but he refused to acknowledge the doubts that tried to unman him. He took only his rifle and ammunition and the clothes he was wearing.

At this point the shore consisted of a beach backed by a steep embankment which Jean tried unsuccessfully to climb, then turned down the beach searching for a break. He found it in the form of a small stream which had cut through and won free to the lake. The ditch was too steep and muddy to negotiate, so Jean stepped into the stream and walked up the stream bed in knee-deep water. His feet had been numb for an hour in the snowmelt and now that numbness crept upward.

Out on top he was in a low jungle of mixed bushes, none of which were more than man-height and all of which had grown since the melt began. The first sprigs of gluegrass were appearing but would not become a gummy carpet until the waters had further receded. He could not see twenty meters ahead.

Here he would hunt. Here the reduced visibility gave even a slow-moving cripple a chance to blunder upon game. Of course, hunting alone like this he was not likely to survive long, but at least he could go out like a man.

Twenty minutes later something stirred in the bushes before him. Moving inland meant moving westward into the prevailing wind, so Jean could reasonably expect to catch the animal unawares. He moved carefully through the ankle-deep mud.

Trihorns! Of the creatures he might meet, only the longnecks were more dangerous. Jean faded back into a clump of siskal and waited, his rifle ready. There was a bull with two cows, all in full antler, along with three calves. He could probably kill the bull with his first shot; he might kill one cow with his untried underbarrel. Even if he were that fortunate, the other cow would kill him.

He was sorely tempted. Here would be a fitting end

for a man and a hunter. He sighted on the bull, his finger caressing the trigger, but did not fire.

After a time the trihorns wandered away, the cows having sensed something strange in the area. Trihorn belligerence is matched only by trihorn caution, so the beasts drifted off to the north.

Jean sat beneath the siskal, chewing a fresh stalk and thinking. He tried to unravel what had held his finger. It was partly because of what he had glimpsed on the island—the possibility of an existence where killing did not reign supreme. It was also partly the influence of Levi-Stuer who had preached that being a man was more than merely being a hunter. Part of his hesitation was due to his own thinking as well. He had done things that no man had done before. No brave hunter from the colony had ever dared the lake or sought out the secret of the disappearing herds, yet he, a cripple, had done so. His impulses had been largely self-destructive, true, but they were not so any longer. He had faced death and therein found the courage to face life.

When he crawled out of the bushes and set off he limped no less but was somehow less conscious of it.

He had not found new self-worth in a moment, but in a moment he had realized the culmination of that which had been building for a year. He was a *man;* let others think what they wished—he knew his own worth.

And having so reestablished his own worth, his loneliness was thereby intensified.

Firelight flickered in the night. Jean lay against the backrest of lal that he had woven, contemplating the fire and the various night sounds beyond. His belly was full to repletion and a massive hunk of humpox meat hung beside the fire, slowly drying and cooking. The carcass that had given up this meat lay nearly a half kilometer to the west and was doubtless even now being stripped by longnecks and krats. Jean had killed early in the afternoon and had lost no time getting what meat he could eat and retreating before the carnivores arrived.

His rifle, carefully recharged, lay across his knees. Behind him was a shallow pool which would give warning splashs if anything tried to reach him from that side. He did not even bother to turn his head in that direction. Ahead the ground fell away from the hummock he had chosen and any carnivores out there would be wary of the fire. Of course he dared not sleep until he returned to the gig and put safely out into the lake. That he would do in the morning, for he had much to think about tonight.

He had found the herds, which had been his ostensible purpose. Now he could return to the colony with his findings. Yet he knew that few would be interested, for it would be knowledge without practical import.

For the first time since his injury, he was lonely for humankind. Even during the year he had spent with Levi-Stuer he had shunned his fellows. Now he was transformed, though outwardly unchanged. It had been a slow process, but he had established a deeper acquaintance with himself and a truer picture of his abilities and failings.

He had no illusions about his fellow man, however. They would no more accept him now than they had before. This then was his dilemma, that he had progressed beyond his fellows and was thereby cast out.

Beyond the firelight, eyes watched him. Yellow, slitted eyes on a finely sculpted head—longneck. Other eyes watched him as well, brown eyes like his own, set in a human face.

Vapor slipped away from the fire after half an hour. By that time he knew everything that could be learned from it. The aroma of the meat told him that it was humpox and the absence of caterwauling nearby told him that the stranger had sense enough to make camp far from the scene of his kill. He carried a muzzleloading rifle, but of a different design from those Vapor had seen before.

The other wore a full beard and shaggy hair, neither yet streaked with gray, though his face was lined with worry or some great sorrow, giving him the false appearance of age. He had been injured at some time in the past, for he unconsciously stroked his left thigh in the manner of one remembering some old pain.

His clothing was of fur, of course, but much more conservatively cut than that which Vapor's people wore. Also it was quite heavy and the fire was high. Perhaps this one was ill or he was not inured to the climate or he did not know how to avoid the carnivores at night. Perhaps a combination of these factors existed.

Vapor was curious, but Grandaddy Longneck was getting too close for comfort. Vapor could smell the creature upwind of where he lay. It would not do to become careless while watching the stranger. He slipped away into the night.

By first light he was backtracking the stranger and soon he reached the humpox. Only bones and tattered hide remained. Vapor made a large circle about the site in order to get beyond the area which the carnivores had churned. There he found the stranger's back trail again and followed it toward the lake.

Vapor was amazed at what he read in the mud. The stranger was a cripple! His right footprint was uniformly deeper than his left and showed a dragging trail where he lurched each time his left foot was down. His left footprint was shallow and smudged where he twisted to thrust his good leg forward. That such a one should be here was incredible.

He soon observed the lurching gait for himself as he came up behind Jean making his way toward the lake. Vapor followed close behind, chafing at the slowness of their progress.

The stranger reached the bluff overlooking the lake and turned north, worked his way to the beach down a stream and turned north again. Vapor stayed on the embankment out of sight. Then he saw how the stranger had come and at the same time realized that he was about to get a new insight into his character.

He had come by boat, but he would not leave in

that manner, for the gig remained only as memory and a scattering of shattered staves and timbers. Vapor could read the story in the mud even from the embankment above. A small herd of trihorns had been spooked by a pair of longnecks and had stampeded down the beach, running over the boat in the darkness and in their panic.

The stranger broke into a lurching trot, then stopped dead. Vapor settled down to see how he would handle this new situation.

Jean's emotions ran the gamut, from disbelief to anger, to self-recrimination, to fear, to grief, and back to disbelief. The gig was shattered beyond repair and scattered over three-hundred meters of beach.

He dropped down on a broken stave and sat inert. Slowly he forced himself to consider the meaning and implications of his plight.

Jean could not return, yet he had not entirely planned to return. He realized then that he had been thinking, in the back of his mind, of returning to the island, to the abode of peace, there to spend his life in the company of the semihuman dilwildi. The fear that had driven him away had abated over the subsequent weeks, but he had not acknowledged his plans even to himself.

Now he could not return to the island, nor could he return to the colony by water. The wood in the gig would not make a raft even if he could recover it all, and there were no trees here. Perhaps there were trees in the mountains that his map had shown to be several hundred kilometers to the west, but there was no way he could reach them, nor cut them down, nor return them to the lake. The bushes that grew during the melt were all but useless for wood.

He could not go by water and he could not remain where he was. Soon the melt would pass, and he would starve here. Without shovels he could not dig a permafrost cellar, nor could he hope to fill one while hunting alone. He would starve if he remained, nor did he wish to remain cut off from his fellows in such a desolate place. Solitude might have been acceptable amid the beauty of the island but not here.

He would follow the herds. There was no other hope.

For years the younger colonists had speculated whether the *others* lived nearby or followed the herds. Only a few would champion the latter position. It seemed absurd that anyone could survive constant migration, or that anyone could trek so many kilometers every year. Now Jean would get a chance to prove or disprove the theory. It was not a prospect that pleased him.

He searched through the wreckage of the gig, recovering his few belongings. These he bundled together and then he laid out the torn sail. It was too large to carry so he carefully cut out a sleeping robe from the best of it and then sat before a fire made of the pieces of his gig and made himself a fresh pair of moccasins from part of the remainder.

As he sat, he calculated that the melt moved at an average rate of thirty-five kilometers per day. He would be hard pressed to maintain that pace day after day, especially since he would also have to hunt and avoid being hunted at the same time.

He would not survive. Somewhere he would be too slow and a trihorn or longneck would get him. Or he would run out of ammunition. Or, worst of all and most likely, his leg would not let him keep up the pace and he would slowly fall behind the melt until low winter and starvation overtook him.

If so, so be it. His earlier shock had given way to a new fatalism. His one great adventure was ended and an even greater one had begun. It would be better to die thus than to have lived out a miserable life as a half-man in the colony. Yet he did not look forward to death as he had before, for it would be sweeter still to survive and return.

Night was about him and the fire was low. He had not slept the night before and now he must. He might die from sleeping, but there was no help for it. He put his finger through the trigger guard, his thumb on the hammer, and let go of consciousness.

Chapter 14

The first day, Jean merely walked. He had enough meat for at least three days and he gathered such fruits as he came across on his trek. During the morning he kept to the lake shore, but about noon he came to a small river which he could not cross and turned inland.

This was the first obstacle he had encountered and already he was wondering if it were not insuperable. He had no boat and could not swim with his bad leg. There were no logs with which to make a raft. By nightfall he was far inland and no better off than he had been. Finally he burrowed into a thicket of dry greenhorn, a remnant of the last melt, and wrapped himself in the remains of the sail. He had to have sleep so he trusted the greenhorn to give warning of the approach of any animal. Three times during the night he was wakened by something rustling in the dry brush, but each creature retreated when he shouted.

In the morning he hunted again, even though he needed no meat. This time he carefully removed and emptied the herby's stomach, tied off one end, and inflated it. With fresh meat and his few possessions wrapped in the sail and his rifle and ammunition held high, he floated across the river on the inflated stomach. It was barely buoyant enough to keep his head and rifle above the water.

He had lost time going upriver so he made no move to return to the lake. Nothing was there for him now. All day he walked, dragging his bad leg in ankle-deep mud, splashing clumsily through knee-deep pools of snowmelt. He was constantly cold from the wet.

That night he was close to despair. His leg throbbed unmercifully and he had walked past sundown looking for another dry brush thicket. He had found none, and now he dared not sleep for fear of longnecks. He wrapped himself in the sail and sat cross-legged atop a bare knoll; he had no fire for nothing was dry enough to burn. His rifle lay across his knees as he struggled to stay awake. The cold that had been with him all day intensified now. His head nodded and soon he was asleep.

What woke him he could not have said, but when he opened his eyes he was looking into the snarling face of a longneck. The creature had been overcome with curiosity at his strange figure and had not attacked at once. Jean grabbed convulsively for his rifle, thumbing the hammer and squeezing the trigger in one motion. In his haste he grabbed the forward hammer and the 17mm short barrel went off like a small cannon, blowing a gratifyingly large hole in the carnivore and shocking the night into wakefulness.

He sat for a long time with the longneck at his feet, the blood black in the wan moonlight, shivering uncontrollably. Then he slit the hide and ate, the still warm juices returning life to his frozen body. Nothing moved. Jean got to his feet and surveyed the night-world around him. In every direction the world was a shallow lake, save for his low hillock. He should leave the place because the smell of blood would soon attract other predators, but to do so would be to expose himself again to the numbing waters.

Working carefully in the uncertain moonlight, he reloaded the lower barrel, thanking the fates that had sent his finger to that heavier charge. He had fired two shots here and one on the island, all from the upper barrel. This was the first shot from the lower. He could not continue to use his rifle in this manner if he were to survive the half year it would take him to return to the colony.

He should move out, he thought, but he could not

face the snowmelt. Instead, with rifle ready he sat at the part of the hillock furthest removed from the longneck's carcass.

Several things were apparent. He needed waterproof footwear if he was to survive, for the continual wetting would lead to pneumonia and death. It must be made with care, tightly sewn and well greased. He needed a fine hide—the longneck would provide that—and a fat animal from which to render lard. The herby he had killed would have provided grease, had he known that he would need it. Jean would also need a fine bone awl or needle and patience.

It was also apparent, and even more pressing, that he must find a way to sleep without being attacked. So far he had done poorly—almost fatally poorly. Finally, he had to find a way to conserve his ammunition.

When morning came, he ate longneck meat and removed the hide, carefully scraping the inside and rolling it into a bundle. He took a rib to make an awl and started north.

Whatever else he did, every day must carry him onward. Were he to become injured or ill, the melt would pass him by and he would starve.

He cut wands of siskal, lal, and greenhorn as he walked and stripped them of their bark. The colonists had never had to discover which native woods would make bows for they fabricated fiberglass bows in the landing craft's small workshop. Now he would experiment.

He stopped early that night about half a kilometer past a thicket of dry brush and built a good-sized fire. He hung his bow staves to cure, then cooked herby meat, now slightly high, and the remainder of the longneck. He sliced the meat thin and hung it over the fire on green branches, watching it carefully so that it dried without burning. The result was poor jerky, lacking salt and not having had the time to cure properly, but at least it gave him some emergency supplies. He alternated watching the fire, the meat, and the bow staves and working on the longneck hide. When nightfall was near he killed the fire and retreated to the brush for the night.

He had lost time and he knew it, but it had been necessary. He hiked straight through the next day, eating dried meat and the seeds and fruits that he found and by nightfall felt that he had gained some distance. Again his leg throbbed, though perhaps not so much as before. Near nightfall he stalked and killed a big trihorn.

Once again he did not sleep, but sat the night through beside the carcass, working by firelight to jerk the meat and preserve the hide. It was for the hide that he had killed the animal.

In the morning he started out under the burden of the trihorn hide, carrying three strung bows. Throughout the day he tried them, firing cut reeds at impromptu targets and concluded that the greenhorn was too limber for use. The siskal broke during the morning. The lal was a poor bow wood, but he could do no better.

In the afternoon he cut numerous wands of greenhorn and when he reached a knoll he worked through the night for a second time, scraping, curing, and sewing on the project for which he had sacrificed so much.

It was apparent to Vapor that the stranger was a colonist and might therefore present a threat. He was a cripple, however, and despite the fine rifle he carried he was no personal threat. The threat lay in what he represented; was he the first of a new wave spreading out to endanger Vapor's people?

By now Vapor was convinced that this was no ordinary colonist. He had a strange self-sufficiency that no other colonist had ever shown. He lived on the land, not separated from it by walls of timber. When his boat had been destroyed, he had not panicked but had immediately begun a northward trek.

Only once since then had Vapor left him. He had crossed Mist-on-water's trail and had run his sister down to tell of this new wonder so that the information could be relayed to the tribe. Then he had returned to his role of unseen observer.

Once the stranger had wasted an afternoon drying meat and curing wood and hides, but otherwise he had made steady progress. He had made crude bows and found them wanting. Vapor's own bow was a laminate of greenhorn and lal joined by a glue made from trihorn hooves. It would cast an arrow swiftly and with power. A man could hunt with it, though not alone and certainly not if he were a cripple. Vapor wondered just what the stranger planned to do with his crude bows and why he bothered with them when he had a rifle.

For two nights now the stranger had not slept. It was plain that he had not learned to extract the juice of the siskal root to make a warding amulet and was therefore unable to trust himself to the mercies of the night. Vapor himself woke several times during the night to watch the work in progress, but he could not understand its meaning.

When morning came, Vapor could see that the stranger was dead on his feet and wondered what he would do now. When he saw, he laughed in amazement and admiration at the stranger's imagination. He had made a bowl-shaped framework of greenhorn and now he stretched the trihorn hide over it and lashed it tight. Then he turned it over and carried it to the shallow lake of snowmelt. It was apparent that this was why he had stopped in this particular place. Carefully loading his gear aboard, he pushed his makeshift coracle away from shore and poled to the center of the lake. There he dropped a stone anchor overside and lay down to sleep in comparative security.

Jean woke a few hours before sunup and poled to shore. He had slept eighteen hours, nearly an entire planet day. By moonlight he broke down and bundled his coracle and started out. He had made several kilometers by the time the sun rose and he walked the day through, rebuilding his coracle in the dusk. The next day he repeated the process, still eating dried meat and the fruits which hung everywhere. He stopped early the third day to hunt and quick-jerk the meat of a herby.

He thought he was doing all right, but he had no way to know. If he marched too quickly he would eventually reach the forefront of the melt and would need only to lay over one or two days to be back at the peak. If he marched too slowly, however, he would soon find game and fruit becoming scarce. So far he could detect no change either way.

His leg still hurt constantly, but not with the same intensity. He seemed to be getting into the swing of the long march and he felt good, save for a loneliness that became more intense with each kilometer.

Three weeks passed and the game became less plentiful, with a greater proportion of leers. Then he saw his first snow and he fell on his knees before it and gave thanks. He was marching *faster* than the melt! Overcome with relief, tears coursed down his cheeks.

Jean celebrated by killing a trihorn. He laid over for two days, curing the hide to replace the fast-failing one on his coracle and jerking the meat. Trihorn was a treat after a diet that had consisted almost entirely of herbys, which were easier to kill. If only he could find some way to conserve his ammunition, he would be satisfied, but so far he had been unable to kill with his bow. To come within effective bowshot of a wary animal required better stalking than his leg allowed.

He was only slightly worried, though. It would take, he figured, about two hundred days to reach the colony and he was killing only every third day, now that he had established a system of drying meat. With the coracle to sleep in, he had not had to fire in self-defense in three weeks. That came partly from his increasing prowess as an outdoorsman; he knew now the little tricks of staying out of harm's way. He should be able to get to the colony on his remaining ammunition.

But there was no margin for error. He must not shoot without scoring a kill and he must not get himself into a position where he had to fire to preserve his life, or where he had to kill more than one animal at a time. Leers were out and trihorns could only be taken when he found a solitary bull grazing away from his harem. Mostly he must live on the fleet but harmless herbys.

By the end of the second day, the vegetation around him had become slightly more lush and he had cured the hide, replacing the old one on the coracle. When he put out into the water that night he felt well satisfied.

Nightwind came to relieve Vapor of his self-appointed guard duty. He dropped beside Vapor on the dry knoll and stripped off thigh-high waterproof moccasins. "What has happened?"

Vapor offered a piece of meat from the fire. "The stranger has decided that he is outrunning the melt and has laid over. He has smoked meat and is sleeping on the water."

"What?"

Vapor explained about the coracle. Nightwind was incredulous and slipped away to see for himself. When he returned he laughed and called the stranger a crazy one. Vapor shook his head. "No. He does not have a warding amulet." Vapor touched the aromatic bag that hung in the trees, giving off a scent which was faint to their human noses but horrific to the native fauna. "How would you sleep at night without one?"

Nightwind considered and agreed that the stranger was not so crazy after all. "Vapor, the council would hear you speak of this one. They wish to know whether it would be better to approach, ignore, or kill him."

Vapor nodded. This was the message he had expected when Nightwind arrived and he was anxious to return. He had taken this reconnaissance on himself, nor would anyone have ordered him to it. The tribe consisted of individuals who cooperated readily enough but were violently independent. Now he wanted to milk his weary weeks for all the glory they would afford. "I will go at once. Will you stay to watch the stranger?" Nightwind said that he would and Vapor took up his amulet and set out at a soggy trot along his back trail.

Nightwind had agreed to watch the stranger, but he was not bound to do so in the same manner that Vapor had chosen. Vapor had remained out of sight; Nightwind was more inclined to give the stranger something to chew on. He slipped back into his moccasins as soon as Vapor's footsteps had retreated, then walked noiselessly down to the edge of the lake. There, in the center of the stranger's firepit, he thrust his ornate spear.

Jean woke late and lay for a time, lulled by the gentle motion of the coracle. He was secure now in his ability to survive—always barring accidents—and for the first time he could relax and let some of the tensions of the last weeks drain away. The melt was a beautiful time—or a beautiful place, depending on one's orientation. For the colonists it was a time, a season of excitement, of blood and meat, of planting and harvesting. During the melt, the colony rose from its cranky somnolence to prodigious feats of labor, only to sink into lethargy for another year when the melt had passed.

But the melt was always present somewhere on the planet; in Jean's new perspective it was not a time but a place, a moving, eternal spring. The colonists never saw the beauty of the melt for they were too deeply engrossed in harvesting what it offered against the bleak months of winter. While Jean had trekked north, busy with his own survival, the beauty of the place/time had soaked into him, making him thankful for the misfortune that had forced him to follow the melt. Now, lying quietly in the coracle, he watched the sun rise and drive away the night's chill. The edges of the water were lacy with ice here on the forefront of the melt, making delicate patterns of sun-sparkle. All around him were the waxy yellow lal flowers growing on the fast-sprouting bushes, mingled with the green of new leaves. If he stayed in place for many more days the yellow would be supplanted by the red siskal flowers and the purple of the greenhorn, but he need only trek hard once again to reach this region of yellow where the leer abounds and the melt makes war on the last regiments of snow. He felt a curious peace and luxuriated in the beauty around him. His only tempering sadness was that he alone was present to watch the miracle that was the melt.

Surfeited with laziness, he poled to the water's edge.

He stopped, the pole dripping forgotten in his hand. There, thrust into the ashes of yesterday's fire stood a proud, feather-ornamented, steel-bladed lance.

Chapter 15

Following Nightwind's instructions, Vapor soon reached the tribe. They were camped on a hillock overlooking a shallow lake where the children were playing with boats of bundled reeds and floating on inflated trihorn stomachs. The smoke from the central fire rose in a cloud, driving back the tiny insects that plague a man, and the scent of several dozen personal amulets made the air slightly acrid.

The barges were drawn up to dry and the elders were gathered in their customary place of comfort near the fire. Vapor could smell the cooking humpox and herby. He was greeted with shouts and teasing as he trotted into camp and Mist-on-water handed her brother a large chunk of steaming meat which he then carried to the fire.

His mother greeted him with a kiss, then let him have several bites in peace before she began her interrogation. She was a strong woman and one of the most outspoken of the elders. Vapor was very proud of her and no less proud of his dark, taciturn father.

"Tell us of this stranger. Is he a colonist?"

"Yes, mother, but a strange one. He is self-sufficient. He lives in the world, not hiding in a burrow, and he came across the lake to this place."

"Searching for what?"

"I do not know, but he has adapted well and looks likely to survive."

She fed the fire as she considered. "I wonder what is his purpose here?"

"There is one way to know."

"Ask him?" She seemed amused.

"Yes."

"And if we do not like his answer?"

"Kill him; but I think that his answer will suit." Vapor paused dramatically, "He is a cripple, you know."

She looked at him suddenly and he realized that she read some message there that he had not meant to convey. "How is he crippled?"

"His left leg is stiff from some old wound and gives him pain."

"How does he bear it?"

"Well."

"What color is his hair?"

Now Vapor knew something was up. "Pale yellow, like Mud-runner's."

"Ah!" She seemed both surprised and pleased. "I told him to take the child, but he would not listen. I told him that the boy was a true son of his father."

"What?"

"The Old Man, you fool, the Old Man. Do you think his hair was always white?"

Jean stared at the lance, completely bewildered. His first thought was that some colonist was here; his second thought was that he had unknowingly returned to the vicinity of the colony. Then he realized that it belonged to one of the *others*.

Who were the *others*? The elders would not discuss

them and Jean only knew that from time to time, always during the hunts, children or young women would turn up missing and their disappearances were always attributed to the amorphous *others*. Were they the winged people, or yet another intelligent species? Or were the disappearances engineered by the *presence* he had known on the island?

Jean pulled the lance free and examined it. It was of some wood he did not recognize, certainly not lal, siskal, or greenhorn. Something from the mountains, then. It was adorned with leer feathers and paint in bands of many colors and headed by a fine blade of iron. That the blade had been fashioned with care was obvious.

Why was it here? Someone/thing had left it, of course, but for what purpose? To see what he would do? To exchange it for something of his?

He had nothing to match its quality except his rifle or his blade, both of which were indispensable. Finally he took a fishhook, line, and sinker from his supplies and draped them over the spear as an offering. Whoever wanted to contact him would have no difficulty in doing so and Jean's leg would make it impossible to track that one down. Nevertheless, he took time to examine the tracks left by the spear's owner. Moccasins; he memorized their design, rolled his coracle, and went on. If the owner of the spear wanted an interview, the opportunity was his. As for Jean, he would simply go about his daily routine.

Nightwind was pleased. The stranger had not taken the lance; therefore he was either honest or cautious. He had left a gift and a fine one. The fishhook was obviously of offworld manufacture and therefore to be treasured. In leaving a gift the colonist had shown himself to be generous—or cautious. He had not left a gift of meat to taunt Nightwind's hunting prowess, nor had he tried to lie in ambush.

Nightwind hefted his spear and trotted after Jean, thinking to devise other tests. It was not to be.

Jean woke to the gentle rocking of the coracle and the first slant of sunlight. He was uneasy about the lance he had found the previous morning and when he raised himself to look toward shore his uneasiness proved itself. This morning he saw not a lance but a dozen moving human forms. They waited for him to pole to shore.

For an instant he considered poling to the opposite end of the pond and running—where? The futility of that action was so apparent that he discarded the thought as soon as it formed.

Trying to seem unafraid, he poled directly toward the crowd on the shore. His heart beat heavily with both fear and anticipation. He had seen no human face for many months.

At the center of the group stood one commanding figure, a gray-haired woman. Her physical stature was slight, but she radiated confidence and authority. At her side stood what had once been a mighty man, very dark and short, now stooped with age. Beyond him stood a young man of Jean's age, his face welcoming, and another of the same age but less friendly. This last one carried the lance Jean had seen the morning before.

Jean grounded the coracle, noting how the remainder of the party held back, and staggered ashore, shamed by the clumsiness his wound engendered. He faced them across a little space, his finger on the trigger of his rifle, both hammers cocked. The woman noted this and smiled. "Welcome home, Jean Dubois. I am Helene Dumezil."

Chapter 16

Jean had traveled with the *others,* who referred to their collectivity as the tribe, for three weeks before the Old Man returned. The Old Man got his name not because he was especially old, but through his singular character. He was not the *Old* Man, but *the* Old Man. He was Jan Andrax and he was Jean's father.

Helene had explained it all. The refugees from old Marcel Dumezil's pogrom had taken to the hills knowing they were too few to survive. When the melt returned and the hunters left the colony, Jandrax—Jean still thought of him by the name the colonists called him—and Sabine Conners had stolen all the children under the age of six, and the refugees and the kidnapped children had gone on to follow the melt. They had been on the move ever since. Helene remembered twenty-two separate circuits and they had long since come to know their trek as well as a farmer knows his fields.

Jandrax had outdone himself. Every member of the tribe, however young, whichever sex, had learned at his knee. All were trained in scoutlore and geology, geography, natural history, and survival on the planet they called simply—the land.

On the second circuit, Jandrax had spent three days hiding in the rafters of a house in the colony and none had known of his presence. He learned that Angi Dumezil and Lucien Dubois had married, knew they had an infant son, and knew, by simple arithmetic, the son was not Lucien's but his.

136

Helene had advised him to steal the child and had offered to raise it herself but Jandrax refused. He still loved Angi, Helene was sure, and would not deprive her of her child. Jan watched the lad's growth each year. He saw his son become a toddler, then an adolescent, then a man. Then he saw him as a man preparing for the hunt.

The last circuit he had not seen him at all, but the rumors were there for any who chose to listen outside the hunting kraals. It was a game that the young ones played for fun and the elders for information. Jandrax learned that his son was now a cripple through the inattention or malice of another and that he had disappeared.

Jandrax had told no one but Helene and Valikili. Even his wives did not know what had happened to his first born, and old Henri, the other surviving elder, was too senile to trust with the information.

Jandrax had many sons and daughters by his two living wives and by his first wife, now dead. In the early years, the refugees stole wives as they needed them and Marie and Helene had not objected, for survival had depended on increasing their numbers. Still, Jandrax was concerned for his firstborn, probably in part out of memory of Angi. When Vapor told his tale, Helene had known immediately that the stranger was Jean.

Jean in turn told his story. Helene was impressed and the youngsters, who were constantly underfoot, were enthralled. Even those of his own generation gave him respect, though they smiled their skepticism of the events on the island.

Vapor and Jean became friends of a sort, but Nightwind remained distant. They were of the first children stolen from the colony, though they remembered only the tribe and the marches. Nightwind in turn had taken a wife from the daughters of the colony—Paulette Dumezil.

She was called Moccasin for some reason Jean could not comprehend. All of the tribe except the elders took fanciful names for themselves. Why Nightwind had taken Paulette instead of one of the girls of the tribe was a mystery to Jean. She was quiet and reserved, clearly a captive rather than a member of the tribe, while the others were laughing and forward. Jean was quite unused to their actions.

One, called Mist-on-water, was particularly trying. She never failed to show off her prowess with a bow or lance in Jean's presence and offered twice daily to best him in a wrestling match, ignoring his crippled condition. It shamed him as nothing had done before and bewildered him as well. Helene watched the proceedings out of wise old eyes that told nothing.

Jean could not get Mist out of his mind, nor could he forget Paulette. His training cried out for him to rescue Paulette from her slavery but he was powerless to do so. He tried to get near enough to speak to her on several occasions, but it was a danger to do so for she was Nightwind's woman. She in turn evaded him, perhaps in shame.

Jean kept up with the company well enough but could not hunt with them. They hunted in quintets; two would go out without warding amulets while the other three would circle about scaring game toward the waiters. Then all five would close in to share the kill if the animal was dangerous.

They did not need rifles and Jean felt worse than useless. Twice he slipped away in the night and stalked a herby or humpox, killing them with his rifle along the path the tribe must take.

The elders did not make the trek entirely afoot, though Helene and Valikili were fit enough. They often rode in the flatboats made from light wood cut in the mountains and drawn by domesticated herbys. These creatures were another of Jandrax's triumphs and they made the nomadic life easier by serving as beasts of burden. Domestic herbys were not eaten since there was an abundance of wildlife to serve that purpose. The boats were slim, flat boxes which would float in water and could be dragged like sleds through mud, allowing them to be used in the two media which were the natural habitat of the tribe.

The Old Man had gone off alone as he was wont to do and none of the tribe worried for him. Of them all, he was the fittest and the one most immune to discipline. His fierce independence had affected them all. He would return when he chose, bringing with him prime furs, or precious wood for the repair of the flatboats, or perhaps some *precursor* relic.

Jean became a mass of illconcealed excitement at the mention of the *precursors,* but the tribe took them in stride. Jandrax had found numerous ruins of an ancient civilization and was always looking for more. What, Jean wondered, would he say to his son's tale of the island?

Jean sat beside the fire one night as Vapor made the rounds of the young girls, teasing each in turn and caressing where they would allow it. The girls were as fiercely independent as their brothers and their prowess as hunters and survivors was no less. Vapor dropped beside Jean with a grin and began his customary teasing. As always Jean took it in serious silence.

"Jean Dubois. What a name; you need a good name like mine. Vapor—now *there* is a name."

"Vapor is the promise of substance which fades away when confronted," called one of the girls who was watching from the edge of the firelight. Vapor snarled back at her, then turned his attention back to Jean.

"Let's see, what would be a good name for you? Turtle for your speed, hey. I've never seen a turtle, but you remind me of the tales the Old Man tells."

"I am happy with my name as it is."

"Ha, girls, do you hear that? I try to do him a favor and he is 'happy with my name as it is,' " Vapor mocked. "What you need is a name to suit you. Let's see, Mud? No. Herby? No, you aren't domesticated." The girls broke into laughter at this.

"I know what I'll call you—Stubborn. Then every time you refuse to answer to your name you will be proving it."

Jean looked straight at Vapor and said, "Go ahead.

139

Call me Stubborn and I'll call you Big-mouth-without-teeth."

Vapor dissolved into laughter, rolling on the ground and leaping up to pound Jean on the back. Jean smiled within himself; he was learning to hold his own with these wildly independent people. He knew that his solitary march had been watched for weeks before he was contacted and that if he had not made it on his own, they would not even have bothered burying him. But he *had* made it and they were willing to accept him because he had shown himself not to need them. It was backward logic by his own lifeway, but he respected and understood it.

Mist-on-water stood up and cast her knife aside. Even around the fire the tribe seldom went unarmed. "Stubborn-Jean," she said, "I think I'll call you Afraid-of-women. Eleven times I have said that I wrestle better than you and eleven times I have been spurned. I swear, Stubborn-Jean-afraid-of-women, that I will never ask you again."

Jean realized that the entire camp was silent, watching, and he knew that there was more to this challenge than met the eye. Helene sat near the fire, watching, her eyes sparkling slightly. He stood up, casting his blade aside also. Vapor whooped and Mist-on-water charged.

She hit him low on the left side, driving her shoulder into his scarred thigh and striking up at his crotch with her fist. Completely unprepared for this, Jean took both blows and went down in agony. His head swam and his throat tightened on the surge his stomach sent rising. He rolled over and looked up to where she stood, legs straddled, her firm breasts pushing against her fur vest, head cocked to one side, taunting. The others were hooting their derision.

He staggered to his feet and ignored her, starting back toward the fire. All around him were taunting voices. Mist turned away in contempt and he moved when she turned, lunging forward on his good leg and reaching for her. His fingers caught in the waistband of her hide trousers and he heaved as he fell, jerking her down so that her rump hit the muddy ground with a splat.

He was upon her before she could retreat and they fought in earnest. She had been schooled by Jandrax himself, but Jean's training had been but little worse and he was both angry and aroused. She was vicious, kicking, biting, and tearing his hair, but he would not be moved. He forced her back to the mud and overcame her.

She lay on her back, panting, and the entire camp was leaping about in mad abandon. He grinned down at her and she smiled, this time without derision.

"Stubborn *would* be a good name for you but I don't think you're afraid of women at all."

"Ha!" came an exclamation from beyond the fire, "I see I got back just in time for the entertainment." The speaker entered the firelight. Jean would have known him even if his express pistol had not hung at his side like a badge of authority. His pale hair had turned white, but otherwise his face and frame were ageless. Jean grinned up at him, never letting go of Mist-on-water's struggling form and said, "Welcome back, *Papa*."

Jan Andrax squatted down beside his son, ignoring his squirming rug, and nodded with satisfaction. "I don't know how you got here, but I'll bet it's some tale."

Jean ate that night with Jandrax and his wives and retold his story, including the details of his encounter on the island. Jandrax shook his head and asked, "Did you tell anyone else this story?"

"Of course. Everyone else has heard it."

"Damn! How did they take it?"

"With skepticism."

"Only skepticism, not outright disbelief?"

"No."

Jandrax cursed. Jean was taken aback by his vehemence. "Come, *Papa*; even Mentor Louis Dumezil recognized the possibility of further enlightenment."

"Jean, we aren't even speaking the same language.

You know that the original crew members were cast out for religious reasons."

"Yes," Jean answered, "But only Nur Mohammet was not a Monist, so Helene told me; you were tarred with the same brush but you surely haven't all become Muslims since then."

Jandrax got up to pace. "Jean, for twenty years Helene has been preaching Monism and I have been scoffing."

Jean was bewildered now. "Are you trying to tell me that you don't accept the Monomythos? That's absurd."

Jandrax opened and closed his hands spasmodically. That old, hated, trapped feeling had returned at this reminder that he was enmeshed in a community too small for anonymity. "I do not believe in your *presence*," he said, "or your winged girl. I do not accept the Monomythos or any supernatural being. I believe only in life, death, and oblivion."

"My God! That's horrible."

"At times, Son. At times—do you want to be a prophet?"

"No!"

"You will be if you don't watch yourself. I have infected the tribe with enough of my discontent to make them susceptible to a new doctrine."

"I am a Monist," Jean snapped. "I don't want to start a new religion."

"Neither did Jesus."

Jean could only shudder at the blasphemy.

"They are ripe for a religion tied to this particular planet. Earth is three planets and five generations removed. They no longer need the Gods of Earth."

"I cannot deny what I have seen."

"Visions always come to lone and lonely men, cast out from their people and suffering great personal tribulations. They are nothing more than projections of unconscious needs in conditions of deprivation."

"No. I saw what I saw."

"I don't believe it."

"And if you are wrong?"

Jandrax scowled still more deeply. "Then I would

truly fear. I have seen what men can do under the *delusion* that they have a god's approval. If they really had it . . . unthinkable!"

In the months that followed, Jandrax and Jean shared in the hunt and in the telling of tales. Jean learned from his father of the *precursor* ruins scattered about Harmony and they speculated on the nature of the *presence*. Jandrax questioned Jean closely about the colony, the details of Angi's life after the purge. They discussed how old Marcel Dumezil had been killed mysteriously in his sleep. Jandrax refused credit for that act and pointed out that it had been done during low winter when the tribe was elsewhere. They speculated as to who might have done it and concluded that it could very well have been his son Anton.

"The other Anton, old Dumezil's grandson, the one who betrayed you. What did you do about him? Did you kill him?" Jean stung under the implied criticism and explained, then added, "How could I challenge him when I don't *know* that he withheld fire? Primers do fail."

"Rarely."

"Rarely—but they do fail and I am not content to take his life while my reasoning may be wrong."

Jandrax merely nodded, offering no advice. "What about your son?"

"Once again, I don't know that he is mine."

"But you are sure in your own mind?"

"Yes."

"What will you do about him?"

Jean shrugged, "I don't know—yet. Before I decide that, I must know if I am welcome here. I am a stranger, after all. My original intention was to return to the colony."

"And now? . . ."

"Now I am not sure. There is little for me there, but I wonder if there is anything for me here. Your people are independent to the point of cruelty. They have your arrogance, but they have never had to face up to the opinions of others. They consider themselves the lords of creation and the colonists as subhumans."

"They accept you."

"Yes, they accept me. But did they ever inquire as to whether or not *I* accept them?"

"Do you?"

"No, not entirely, although I confess a certain respect for their independence. But it it is an independence based on childish bravado and an unwarranted sense of superiority."

Jandrax was silent then, pondering. He stirred his chota and sipped. "It is an old story, Jean, played out on Earth centuries before either of us was born—the story of the nomad and the oasis. The nomad lives his life wild and, he thinks, free, looking down upon the dwellers in the oasis while all the time he is dependent on them. It is thus with us. Likewise the oasis dweller looks with a mixture of fear and derision at the ignorant nomad, whose crude existence lies beyond the pale of civilization."

"You don't depend on the colony."

"No? Where did our women come from?"

Jean waved his hand as if to brush away a side issue. "You have women enough now. Nightwind could have found a woman without kidnapping Paulette."

Jandrax shook his head. "There is more to it than having an equal number of males and females. Our gene pool is too small, not only among us but on the whole planet. We—the tribe and the colonists—need each other. The day will come when we trade together again. I think it is inevitable."

"The elders don't even acknowledge your existence."

"So? We exist. Let them acknowledge or not, they can't keep their children in ignorance forever. Did you not speculate on the disappearances? The day will come when they can no longer ignore us."

Jean showed Mist-on-water how to fire his rifle and she in turn instructed him in the fine points of archery and use of the lance. His leg still hurt with exertion, but he ignored it as always and found that he could hold his own with Vapor and the others as long as they kept their speed to a fast walk. He could not trot or run.

Jean and Mist went hunting using Jean's technique of a slow stalk upwind and she killed a herby with the rifle. No other young member of the tribe had ever fired a rifle and she did an impromptu war dance around the carcass.

The lake lay far to the south and preparations for the turnabout were underway. For weeks the tribe had killed in excess, drying the meat against the flight. Now it came.

The herds had been restless for days. The herbys were milling in the brush, unsure of themselves, and the trihorns were even more belligerent than usual. Longnecks came within sight of the camp and the tribe's children were held close at hand. All nature seethed with the imminent change.

Then they started. Here a humpox turned its shaggy head southward and there a herd of trihorns stampeded nervously, now trotting, now running, south. The herbys were quick on their heels.

The sun was southing. The melt growth still lay untouched to the north but the wildlife had turned away back toward the southeast, cutting away from the crumpled swath they had made and into the dry region of unharvested growth. The sun, too, had turned south, but there was no snow to melt. Snow there was —for it had followed the melt—but it lay far to the south and the herds were hurrying on to find it.

Some of the animals continued north. Always there were a few less gifted with instinctive intelligence and they went on into a fool's paradise of heavy growth, munching their way toward starvation.

The tribe, too, turned southward. Now the animals were wary and lean. Jandrax could still kill them and now Jean's rifle proved its worth. There was some fresh meat and some dried fruit and seeds, but mostly the tribe subsisted on the meat that they had dried in previous weeks.

They moved at the speed of the sun and even the

tribe's boisterousness was subdued by the barren land. It was low winter for a springtime tribe and their spirits were not accustomed to it.

The animals grew gaunt and many died. The children of the tribe ranged wide cutting seedpods for the domestic herbys and the elders rode more now, for they were the first to feel the short rations. Jean's leg hurt constantly and he was hard pressed to keep up and to hunt. Mist-on-water was with him often but had the decency not to comment on the pain she read in his face.

They came to the region of scanty growth. Snow had fallen here, though not in abundance, and every day southward brought them to greater moisture. It was not the unfolding of the melt as the colonists experienced it, for every day saw them in the latitude of the lal, but each day there were more young shoots and soon the headlong flight had slowed to the even pace of the long march.

Jean felt more at one with the tribe for their shared tribulation. He had been wrong in characterizing them as the children of eternal spring, for this ordeal was theirs twice yearly.

Now they were heading southward again and every day brought them closer to the colony and—home?

Moccasin looked beautiful in her finely cured hide vest and trousers and her thigh-high white moccasins. By the standards of the tribe, who came near to worshipping fertility, she was even more beautiful for her round belly, sure indication of her pregnancy.

Jean dropped beside her where she knelt at Nightwind's fire. Nightwind was out on a hunt and Jean had chosen to make his advances in full sight of the tribe. He could not chance a clandestine meeting but this might be taken as innocent conversation between childhood friends.

Moccasin looked shocked to see him and turned her face away. Suddenly he was unsure of himself and unwilling to pursue his intentions. "Paulette."

Her head came up sharply. "Do not call me that; I am Moccasin."

"Paulette, do you wish to stay here? Would you rather return to the colony?"

"Why do *you* taunt me; you aren't of the tribe."

"I am not taunting you."

"Are you asking if I want you to rescue me?" She cocked her head in the attitude of derision so often affected by the girls of the tribe.

"Well, what do you offer?"

Now it was Jean's turn to hesitate, for he was not sure how far his duties to her ran. He had known her when they were children and had desired her as a young man, but much had passed between that time and this.

Moccasin gestured toward the others. "They mock me, they belittle me, but my day will come. I have talked to the older women who were captives in their time. They made their own paths here and so can I."

She looked around her again, at the lushness of the eternal melt just visible beyond the firelight. "Could I leave all this? This wild freedom, this eternal beauty. Could I exchange all this for a drab wooden cubicle and a man who is brutalized by too much slaughter in one season and too much leisure in the other? I can be one of them," she gestured toward Mist-on-water and her comrades. "How could I ever go back to being what I was?

"Could you?"

Chapter 17

Night closed about the town, enfolding it in arms of darkness. Anton Dumezil, the elder, lay silent in the apartment that his own father had occupied and stared at the ceiling. Anton Dumezil, the younger, lay beside his wife staring likewise. Each wondered in the privacy of his own mind how went the machinations that each had set against the other.

Anton the elder swung his feet to the floor and paced his rickety way about his apartment. His feet crushed the fur of the same rug that Nightwind had wrapped himself in a year earlier. His arthritic hips would not let him sleep, nor would his own son's knowledge of those same hips. He could not hunt again. The preparations had been made, the barges were loaded, the melt was on, but Old Anton would not make his kill this year. His own son was leading barge number one.

His mind rushed back over the years to the night he had stood over his father's corpse, knife in hand. Young Anton didn't have that kind of nerve. He was a weakling. If he wrested power from his father, he would not hold it long.

Old Anton was tired of power, tired of the responsibility of leading his fractious following, but he dared not relinquish it. He had taken this scepter by midnight murder and now he could not let it go if he wished to remain alive.

If only sister Angi lived to give him comfort, or her husband, Lucien, dead these several months of the tuberculosis that ate at him so many years. If only . . .

Young Anton stared at the ceiling in indecision. He suspected that his grandfather's death had been at his father's hand. It was common gossip, softly spoken. He should get up, go quietly to his father's apartment knife in hand and end this foolishness about succession. But he would not. He seethed in impotent fury.

He would not because young Anton had not inherited his father's intelligence or his cunning and he knew it. Whatever he did to end his father's reign would be countered by some unexpected move. Try an assassination and he would find some unseen safeguard. Even if it were not so, the expectation of it was enough to deter him.

But let this hunt pass and he would be able to take

his father's place. Already he was leading the hunt; that was a victory.

Or was it? Had his father planned it all; did he know that his son would not return from the hunt alive? It had happened before.

Cold sweat stood upon young Anton's face as he remembered the wild moments, the instant decision, the withholding of fire that had destroyed Jean Dubois two years ago. Jean Dubois, his rival for Chloe— Chloe the slut, whose soft womanhood had gone to fat and whose affection had gone to hatred.

He had made an instant decision then, one of the few he had ever had the nerve to make. And it had been right, but Dubois lived. If only he had had the nerve to finish what he had started. If only . . .

Again he thought of the day he stood face to face with the crippled Dubois and let him take the antler. It seemed such a small thing then, but in his mind it had grown, had unmanned him. If he had stood his ground then, he could have stood his ground now. But he had not.

There was a disturbance in the air which he would not have noticed had he not been upwrought. There was a stirring of breeze and an excess of light where there should have been only darkness. Softly in the night, Marcel, his son (Dubois's son!), whimpered. Dumezil slipped out of the bed, careful not to waken the shrew that lay beside him, and took up his blade.

He drew back the hide curtain that screened their sleeping area. The shutters were gone from his window and wan moonlight stole in. Someone was in the room!

Some assassin sent by his father?

There was—something—near the door. With his left hand Anton struck a light and touched the wick of a candle.

It was the antler, remade into a cane. It was the very one that had torn Dubois, that Dubois had taken, had carried as a visible goad. It stood against the door, taunting.

No, it could not be! It was a forgery, made and placed at his father's command. It had to be.

Something stood behind him. He tried to turn his head, but could not. He swallowed. He leaped sideways, bringing up his blade.

"Anton, you have something of mine. I have come for it. Stand aside and I will let you live."

Anton's face was sweaty white in the moonlight. He shook his head, but the ghosts would not go away. "No!"

"Yes, Anton. A question, out of curiosity. Did the primer actually fail?"

Dumbly Anton shook his head.

"I have been advised by better men than either of us that I own your life. That I can kill you and feel no qualms of conscience." Jean smiled. "I think you would not even resist me much. But I will not kill you.

"You wanted the antler; you have it. I need it no longer. But I will take my son.

"You, I will let live. Your life would be more punishment than death in any case. Your crippling of me only made me stronger and the prize that you took from me was a thing of no worth—have you enjoyed Chloe?"

Anton trembled at the taunt, but did not advance.

"I will take my child now."

Why Anton did it, Jean never knew. Perhaps he saw his life laid out before him, a half-man who let his own son be stolen. It was the first and last manly act of his life. He leaped forward, his blade raised. Jean slapped it away and thrust his own knife deep between his ribs.

Anton's knees hit the dirt floor with a quiet shock and his eyes were wide. Death came rushing in on him and he turned toward the bed, his hand reaching out for Chloe. He died there, stretched toward that for which he had strived so hard, from which he had received so little. He was stretched thus when she woke to the light of morning and her screams alerted the colony to come see this latest wonder, the returned antler, the bloody floor, the empty crib.

POSTSCRIPT

Standard Year 904 and of the colony, Year 36

When Jean reached the hilltop, Snowmelt had already come and gone. He leaned heavily on his staff and looked first at the rough stone marker, then upward and outward across the endless melt to the lake. After a time, tears came and he let the precious moisture fall upon the earth that covered his father's body. Farewell, Jandrax. No man on this planet has made a mark so uniquely his own.

Snowmelt approached then, shyly, much as Isaac must have approached the alter. Jean smiled down at him, and reached out his hand. Snowmelt touched him fleetingly then withdrew. He scuffed the damp earth with his moccasin. He was slim, brown and powerful. The perfect savage. "Son," Jean said, "I am leaving for a while."

Snowmelt flashed a resentful look. "I know. Back to the island. Everyone is talking about it."

Jean frowned his distaste. "The tribe is making me a prophet, and I never wanted that."

"You claimed to speak to God. Prophet or liar; you left yourself no third alternative."

"I suppose not. Well, I was warned."

"Why are you going? Why must you leave me?"

Jean squinted at the distance and turned his face away to hide the depth of his feelings. "That I cannot answer. Rather, I will not. I will not burden you with it all, though you know part."

Now his son turned away, for to acknowledge that his father was a cripple, to acknowledge that no woman chose to bed with him, was to acknowledge shame on them both. Yet the knowledge would not go away. "Was there never a woman of the tribe who looked favorably upon you?"

"Yes, Son; once. Briefly."

"The winged girl was very beautiful?"

"Yes."

"But she too will have aged."

"Perhaps. Perhaps not."

"And if you go to the island, there will be no way to reenact what happened before. You said yourself that the *presence* rejected you."

"I can only try."

Snowmelt turned blindly toward Jean, unaccustomed tears streaking his face. "If you loved me, you would stay." Jean reached out to him and, for once, Snowmelt allowed himself to be embraced.

"My son! If I did not love you, I would not have stayed these twelve, long, hungry years."

Snowmelt pushed away and turned his back. For a time, Jean let the silence lie between them, then he said, "Will you come to the lakeshore to see me off?"

He shrugged without turning. "I suppose."

"See that you do!" Without looking back, Snowmelt began to descend the hill. Jean let him go. Soon only his shaggy head showed occasionally above the siskal.

Excerpt from the DUBOIS HIEROS.
Manuscript discovered on the planet
Jandrax, galactic coordinates 11C 927C84.

1. In the morning of the world, the hero strove with the winds and cast down the mountains. The wind walker and the cloud dancer moved into the open air and there was rain, and from the rain, grasses, and from the grasses, cattle, and from the cattle, men.

2. The hero lay upon Sinai at the world's edge and dreamed himself a dream.

3. First from the dream came the walker of winds, and he cleaved her to wife.

4. And from out of her loins came all manner of things, both good and evil . . .

About the Author

Syd Logsdon was raised on a farm in Oklahoma, attended college in Michigan, graduate school in Chicago, and served four years as a surgical technician in the Navy. He has worked as a farmer, archaeologist, carpenter, and Red Cross director. He has crisscrossed the United States many times and biked the west coast of California, Washington, and Oregon. Now thirty, he lives in California with his wife Lois, writing full time, and coordinating disaster preparedness for the local Red Cross. He has written four novels to date, of which *Jandrax* is the third.